Self-Publishing SCHOOL

Author Advantage Live

2019

"DIFFERENCE MAKER"

Award Recipient

"Karen's writing is heartfelt, genuine and straight. Her story is hopeful and inspiring. As a survivor myself, I can tell you first hand navigating through this disease is overwhelming, helping our loved ones navigate is even more challenging. So tackling this subject with such clarity is a gift, and something anyone can benefit from. People always want to help in so many wonderful ways when a friend is diagnosed, this book is the place to start! Karen's experiences and insights are spot on... and she lays it all out in a way that is easy and moving to read for such a tough subject... I definitely recommend this book for anyone going through breast cancer, and those that surround them..." Jillian Veran Rezo— Cofounder of the non-profit BeautifulSelf.org, Host of the Sexy Survivor Beauty Segment, and Beauty Expert.

Winning

THE BREAST CANCER BATTLE

Dear Clyd —
So great to know
you through TFL — keep
leading us! Love your spirit!

Love
Always.

Winning
THE BREAST CANCER BATTLE

Empowering Warriors and
Guiding Loved Ones

KAREN IVERSON

Editor: Katie Chambers, Beacon Point
Cover designer: Leslie Hann
Cover image: Karen Iverson

Winning the Breast Cancer Battle: Empowering Warriors and Guiding
Loved Ones

Copyright © 2019 by Karen Iverson

Disclaimer: The information given in this book is based upon the personal opinion of the Author, may not be suitable for every situation, and should be further explored with your doctor. The Author shall not be liable for damages arising here from. The fact that websites are referred to in this work does not mean the Author endorses the information the website may provide or recommendations it may make. Further, readers should be aware Internet websites may have changed since publication of this work.

Library of Congress Cataloging-in-Publication Data

Iverson, Karen
Winning the Breast Cancer Battle: Empowering Warriors and Guiding Loved Ones

ISBN-13: 978-1-7340347-1-4

This book is dedicated to my mother, Anne.

No matter what, she has always stood by me. This ordeal was no exception as she flew up to be by my side more times than I can count. She comforted me on a daily basis over the phone when she couldn't be with me.

Acknowledgements

I would like to sincerely thank Daniel for all of his support throughout this whole process. I hope he knows how imperative he was to my success.

And, then, there's Daniela. True friends stick side-by-side through the thick and the thin. When I need an encouraging word, Daniela has always been and continues to be right there for me.

My friendship with Allison is proof good things come from the bad. Thank you for giving me suggestions whenever I asked and assisting me in the final stages of writing this book.

Thank you to the entire TFL (Tennis for Life) crew. Thank you for all the friendships and for showing me life can still be enjoyable after breast cancer.

Through a photo shoot, Beautiful Self, and the resulting friendships, developed my inner beauty again.

Dr. Janice, you are an inspiration. I am grateful you have partnered with me on this last leg.

Thank you to Jess and Rod for pitching in to complete the book and cover.

To Ramy, thank you for guiding me all along the way. You and the SPS team have enabled this book to come to fruition. I am eternally grateful.

I would also like to thank my editor Katie Chambers at Beacon Point for offering her expertise and doing to this book what I couldn't do myself.

My cover designer: Leslie Hann, I cannot thank enough!

And, Alex, God rest your soul. Thank you.

A Special Invitation

Receive tools from this book FREE!

READ THIS FIRST

Just to say thank you for buying my book, I would like to give you several resources 100% FREE!

Resources include:

30 Day Positive Mindset Challenge Tracker Form

and

Initial Questions to Ask Your Surgeon Form.

To download these FREE resources go to:

www.winningthebreastcancerbattle.com/free

I traveled on an airplane with my grandmother years ago. The flight attendant took interest in us and during a conversation she said:

"If you're blessed and you know it, you're doubly blessed."

I've lived a blessed life despite also facing many down moments. Somehow, something positive will come out of this too.

Contents

Introduction

I never imagined cancer would grab me. My dad, at forty-two, died of lung cancer a week before I turned ten and shortly before my brother turned thirteen. My grandfather died when my dad was thirteen. My dad's cancer wasn't due to smoking, but either way I believed my brother would succumb, too, when his kids were teenagers, just like my dad and granddad. But here instead, at thirty-nine, I faced breast cancer. While breast cancer is said to be "curable," that applies more for the physical body. It is harder to cure the emotional trauma from being a cancer patient or from even caring for a cancer patient. I know how much my father's death left me struggling through life, living in a confused zigzag pattern of uncertainty. I'm concerned other patients and their families and friends, and those who are the specific "caregivers" in their lives, will suffer and struggle as I have. This book is to shed light on how to lessen the suffering patients, family members, friends, and caregivers will face. I am so honored to be the recipient of the 2019 Self-Publishing School "Difference Maker" award which speaks to this mission.

Being a past sufferer myself and having studied English at the University of New Hampshire, holding a master's degree from Columbia University Teachers College, and also having a lifelong love of learning I felt encouraged to share my journey. My knowledge on the subject has included individual experiences, involvement with support groups both in person and online, as well as reading and interacting with doctors, patients, families, and friends.

Cancer is on the rise. Breast cancer specifically is found everywhere: the National Breast Cancer Foundation, Inc. states one in eight women will develop it at some point in their lives. Men can get it too, though it is not as common. Breast cancer, like other cancers, affects the person inflicted physically and mentally and also affects family members, friends, and caregivers. In some ways, it is harder for those not inflicted. No one is immune as almost everyone knows someone who has been struck by cancer.

How do those of us going through it know how to cope and know what questions to ask doctors, nutritionists, nurses, etc.? How do families, friends, and caregivers truly understand what someone with breast cancer is actually going through? How do we not shy away, but instead display confidence in knowing what to say and how we can be helpful?

This book paints an illustration of the truth about breast cancer. *Winning the Breast Cancer Battle: Empowering Warriors and Guiding Loved Ones* will solve these problems by bringing you directly into the life of a sufferer who expresses what it is like in a warmhearted and easy to read manner. It will make clear in your mind the exact experiences a breast cancer patient faces. It offers tips on what the patient needs to know and expect, questions to ask doctors to be best informed, and insights for family members, friends, and caregivers as to what to say and do to be most helpful. All who read it will find this devastating and life-halting disease change into a more manageable one that even involves positive experiences.

The important experiences are included in the diary entries. At the end of each chapter, I have included tips, which relate to the events mentioned, to help the patient cope and allow family members, friends, and caregivers to better empathize and relate to the sufferer. The examples and tips are easily understandable and straightforward in their description. Patients, families, friends, and caregivers have found these passages to be clear and easy to read and comprehend. At the end is a resource list for companies that serve cancer patients, many of which offer free services.

Don't be the person who suffers alone or the one who shies away from precious moments with your loved ones, because you don't know what to say or do. Be the person others are amazed by. Be the person other people see and admire for their courage. Be the kind of person who takes a call to action and makes the effort immediately!

Winning the Breast Cancer Battle will give you positive and long-lasting results. To make a difference in someone's life, continue reading to the very end of the book. Each chapter will inspire you with new insights on how to make the most of each precious moment. Make a difference in your life and a breast cancer sufferer's life by paving the way to survivorship by winning the breast cancer battle.

PART ONE

July

Chapter 1—The Gremlins Inside

Everyone is afraid of something. Sometimes we won't admit it; other times, we don't even realize we're afraid of it. My biggest fear came true when I was thirty-nine. Actually, it probably started way before then, but only came to the surface at thirty-nine. The gremlins were eating me from the inside. Silently replicating until finally I consciously began to know they were there.

Day #1—Getting a Pacemaker

I spoke to Daniela today. Love her so much! Now she has a pacemaker.

Out of the blue Daniela was rushed into emergency surgery. I guess that made me value my life a little bit more, and so I paid attention to the sign I have reminding me to do my monthly breast exam.

I have the sign in my bathroom shower. It even has little punch out circles for each month. Do I do them? No. In fact, I never focused on the sign, until now. Not so hard. I'll do it again next month.

Next Month

I'm taking a shower as usual. I'm doing my monthly breast exam, and I don't want to tell you what happened next. I don't want to face it again.

I found a lump.

It was round and felt like a marble. I don't know what size, maybe a nickel, maybe a dime. It could have even been a quarter. I felt around further and then compared it to my other breast. It stood alone. Maybe I should be happy about that?

It didn't really matter. What mattered was that it was there.

Calling My Doctor

The hardest part was picking up the phone.

But then came the utterance of *the* words; you know, the words you never want to say.

"I think I found a lump . . . in my breast."

 I made an appointment.

How Can You Not Feel It?

I am nervous but my doctor is seeing me and everything will be all right. But it isn't.

She felt my "good" breast first "for reference." Then she felt for the lump I had found. She patted and she felt. She asked me again where the lump was. She patted some more until she came to her conclusion.

"I don't feel anything," she reported nonchalantly.

How can you not feel it? That marble is clear as day!

But since I was thirty-nine and "almost of mammogram age," she wrote a prescription for both my first ever mammogram and breast sonogram. I thank God she at least did that.

Are You Kidding Me Radiology?

My gynecologist referred me to a radiologist. I call them to schedule my first ever mammogram. The next available appointment isn't for a month. No, there isn't anything earlier. They tell me I just have to wait.

Surgeon #1

My radiologist saw the "lump," the undifferentiated mass of cells, in both the sonogram and the mammogram they took and sent me back to my gynecologist who then sent me to several possible surgeons. I choose to go to the center nearest me. As instructed, I bring my scans with me.

They have me change into a short robe and put my belongings in a locker, and then wait in the exam room. It's a pretty standard exam room: bed, chair, four walls . . .

The doctor enters, introduces herself, and looks at the scans. She asks to do a physical exam to feel the lump. Following this, she does another sonogram. And then, she calls Daniel, my friend who has come with me, into the room to explain.

She tells me she wants to do a biopsy immediately.

I'm scared. This is reality suddenly hitting me square in the face. She is the specialist, and *the specialist* wants to biopsy my lump to see what kind of cells are contained inside.

We schedule the biopsy for the next day.

My First Biopsy

I go again to the cancer center where they will do the biopsy.

I change and they bring me into a room.

They tell me they will numb me first, and then do the biopsy. They stick my breast with a needle. It hurts, but I'm a big girl. They dig into my breast. It hurts even more. They continue. More needle and increasing pain, but it's a biopsy of a little bump, how long can it last? Keeping my mouth shut, I try to bear the pain. I tell myself it's almost over, and I don't say anything because I'm a *big girl*, but the pain becomes excruciating. I'm ready to scream and cry at the same time, but still, I don't speak up. I keep saying to myself, *They're almost done, they're almost done.*

When it's over, I tearfully comment on how excruciatingly painful it was, and they ask me why I didn't tell them so they could've numbed me more. I just say, "I kept thinking you were almost done and the pain would go away."

The doctor tells me it could be three or four days for the results. I go home with a still intense pain in my breast.

I Have Breast Cancer

The phone rings. I look at the caller ID—it's the cancer center. I answer and my doctor is on the phone. She tells me point blank: "You have breast cancer." I'm dumbfounded. No, hold on for the worst news of your life, just "The results show you have breast cancer. I want you to come in."

I head over and luckily Daniel is available to come too. The doctor talks about the options: lumpectomies versus mastectomies and she tells me she had breast cancer herself and loves her breasts now more than before because she never liked them. *Is this an attempt to make me feel better? I'm perfectly happy with my breasts.* She continues to talk, but the whole meeting is somewhat of a blur as I still can't grasp the fact that *I. have. Cancer.*

Chapter 1 Tips

Cancer facts

Cancer is when cells in the body decide to duplicate themselves uncontrollably and eventually cause a mass of cells known as a "tumor." The following statistics are from the American Cancer Society, Inc.'s "Cancer Facts & Figures 2019."

- In 2019, there will be an estimated 1,762,450 new cancer cases with 606,880 deaths in the United States.
- Breast cancer is the most common type of cancer for women with 268,600 estimated new cases, which makes up 30 percent of all the new female cancers.
- Of these 268,600 new cases, an estimated 42,260 deaths will occur in 2019, which is only below the "lung and bronchus cancer" category for the most deaths. For men, prostate cancer is the largest diagnosis, accounting for 174,650 estimated newly diagnosed cases in 2019.

Risk factors for breast cancer

These numbers may seem overwhelming, but according to the American Cancer Society (2017), you can do things to lower the risk of getting breast cancer, which are listed below.

First, *drink less alcohol*. Those who drink one alcoholic beverage each day have a slightly increased risk, while those who drink two to three drinks every day have an approximately 20 percent higher risk of developing breast cancer as compared to women who don't drink.

Second, *lose weight*. Because fat tissue makes estrogen, a main component in many breast cancers, being overweight or obese, especially after menopause, puts you more at risk. Being overweight also frequently means higher insulin levels, which is another risk element. The risk is greater for someone who gains weight later in life rather than being overweight since childhood. This also applies more to fat around the waist area.

Third, *be more active*. It is important to be physically active to reduce the risk of developing breast cancer and this is twofold as being active will also lower the amount of fat in the body. The suggested amount of activity is a minimum of 150 minutes of moderate movement or 75 minutes of vigorous exercise spread throughout the week.

Fourth, *becoming pregnant before the age of thirty* seems to reduce the risk of developing breast cancer, except this reduction of risk does not apply to the development of triple-negative breast cancers. And then, *combining pregnancy with breastfeeding* is fifth on the list. It is important to note, though, that breastfeeding needs to be continued for one and a half to two years for this benefit, and this is uncommon in the United States.

Sixth, *do not use certain birth control methods that rely on hormones*. With most birth controls, after ten years post use, the risk decreases.

Seventh, *post-menopausal women shouldn't use hormone therapies,* which are designed to reduce the side effects of menopause.

And, lastly, *reconsider breast implants* as certain types have been linked to a rare cancer so consider this when deciding to invest in implants. These steps can reduce the risk of developing and dying from breast cancer.

Methods to reduce stress

Leading a less stressful life is thought to help reduce the risk of breast cancer as well. So instead of worrying, take action. Share your feelings with family members and friends or seek out the advice of a trained counselor or behavioral health team.

Exercise. Journal. Make Art. Be present in the daily moment; let the future take care of itself. These can help in becoming calmer on a day-to-day basis. Lastly, if it is customary for you to do so, pray and ask others to pray for and with you.

If you have been diagnosed with breast cancer, look into joining a breast cancer support group, or multiple groups, either in person through your cancer center, online, or both! Other group members will talk about their experiences so you will learn vital pieces of information, so you can bounce your ideas off the group. Often medical staff are involved as well, providing their knowledge and support. If you're fifteen- to thirty-nine-years-old there's a group for cancer sufferers in your age range called "Stupid Cancer" that you can join.

It may be hard at the beginning to join a group, but everyone will take you under their wings and tears are always accepted *and usually hugs too!*

There are additional free—or at reduced rates—services offered to those suffering with breast cancer. Besides support groups, cancer centers and hospitals offer, weight lifting programs, yoga classes, tennis groups, vacations, cooking classes, food delivery, and even cleaning services, etc.

Action steps once appointments begin

-Designate one notebook to be used for all of your appointments. My mother used a spiral bound notebook, to take notes at my doctor's appointments so all the notes were together whenever she needed to refer to them. You can do the same thing. It is a good idea to bring someone to the appointments to take notes for you. You may be overwhelmed with the material and may not be able to completely focus on the information provided by the doctors. After each appointment, you can also go over the notes with your loved one, or notetaker, to add in any additional information that may have been left out and any additional questions which may arise to be asked at the next follow up appointment.

-Once you start taking tests, keep copies of all of your reports. You can keep them in a folder, or binder, and take them to all your appointments with your spiral bound notebook.

-Before you go to each appointment, write down all of your questions in your notebook with space for the answers so your notetaker can fill them in at the appointment.

-Add a calendar to your notebook for writing down important dates and times.

Things families, friends, and caregivers can do

-Be the notetaker for the patient.

-Remind them about their appointments and offer to drive them.

-Review and brainstorm thoughts and questions with the patient before and after their appointment.

August

Winning the Breast Cancer Battle

Chapter 2—Reality Strikes

Forced to face the Big C, I now must stare down the changes that are about to completely overwhelm my life. I look straight at my absolutely biggest fear of losing my hair, tell the world about my condition, and look for guidance to uncover some solace along the way. Reality shifts and begins to take on a new meaning.

Meditative Breathing

I'm scared. The truth is, it's physical. It's deep inside.

I could be dying. *The thought hurts.* The unknown.

I focus on my breathing.

Losing My Hair

Because she could not take my health insurance, I am no longer with my first doctor. Before I left her, she informed me that I would definitely need chemo. It would either happen before the lumpectomy to shrink the size of the tumor or afterwards if I ended up having a mastectomy. Either way, I was going to lose a part of my breast, or all of it. No big deal. What was a big deal to me was that I was going to lose my hair. How vain am I? But I bet everyone's first thought would logically be the same after they hear the news about the Big C, right?!

My hair is beautiful: dark brown, long, straight. I can put it up, wear it down, let it blow in the wind, or spread it out across my pillow. It feels sexy when water streams through it. And I've always had it. I can admit a few times I've wanted to chop it off, but that usually was in response to the end of a romantic relationship.

My best friend, Alex, who has been declared cured from melanoma, promises to shave his head with me and tells me it's in vogue for women to go bald these days.

My mother tells me about a website linked to the American Cancer Society that sells wigs and hats. "You've always looked good in hats," she says tenderly.

Later I go on the website. I pick out at least ten hats and "my" wig. I sob the entire time.

Hospital Options

My insurance company doesn't answer on the weekends, and I have some serious concerns. I don't think they are covering anything . . . my computer screen says zero percent. Memorial Sloan Kettering is in New York, and though I'd like to go there, it appears I'm only covered in New Jersey. St Barnabas and Hackensack University Medical Center are both in my network, but again the "zero percent" comes into play so the whole thing may be mute. I'm scared and I'm angry and I don't know what to do and *I can't reach anyone on the phone!*

Telling Daniela

I got upset this morning thinking about telling my friend Daniela about my breast cancer. Why am I upset? She is beautiful. I emulate her and idolize her. And this takes away my womanhood: my breasts and my hair. Why am I so bothered about telling her? I love her; she's one of my closest friends, and I don't want to disappoint her. Now, I'm flawed. Will it change her feelings about me? I'm human; aren't we all flawed? She has heart disease and that didn't change the way I feel about her, but this is external. You don't *see* heart disease, but you will *see* me without hair. And you will *see* my missing breast. It will be different, but it will be fine. My hair will grow back. In fact, I'm told this may just happen to be a blessing in disguise.

Telling My Friends

I have so many supporters; it is such a blessing. My closest friend in school started crying when I told her the news and that I might have to drop out of school. Then, she made a plan for me: She said I was not to drop out. She wanted me standing next to her at graduation. She told me I need to stress less, take yoga, teach again—just a small class—and start doing art again. Next, she insisted I eat healthily too. I know that's the right plan of action, but I also know I can't take on too many new projects right now.

Daniel is waiting for me after my class on the porch with a Corona and lime. How sweet is that? He has been amazing. But now I need to go to bed. I'm tired.

Dear, God, please bless me and keep me well. Amen.

Telling the World

My whole class knows now. In fact, several suspected ever since I found the lump, even before the biopsy. I didn't feel the need to hide it. What good would that do? Some people might want to keep it quiet because of work or not wanting to interrupt family life, but I just blurted it out like a five-year-old girl getting a pony for her sixth birthday only *this* is not a fun occasion!

Everyone has been super supportive and seems to think it's a really big deal, which is news to me because to me it's nothing. Nothing because my brain isn't comprehending what's going to happen to me.

When I was a little girl, my father had cancer. Our parents chose not to tell my brother and me. He was a psychiatrist and had patients who were parents of our classmates. My parents were afraid we would tell our friends, they would tell their parents, and in turn it would affect the patient-doctor relationship.

My situation is different. There isn't anyone I have to hide it from.

I tell my boss today too—my supervisor at my internship—and he is overwhelmingly empathetic.

A Mother's Love

I spoke with Daniela and told her how much my mother means to me. She has been there for me through everything and I don't only mean this. She surprised me by flying up to meet my second doctor, who is now my new surgeon. She told me she's going to be there the day of my surgery too and will stay on for a week. I know I'll want her longer, but her support is always there—be it with her here or on the phone. Daniela agreed.

She will always be welcome in my home. She's the grandma to the only child I've got—my little fur baby.

Facing My Mortality

I want a Coke. I drink it.

I want peanut M&Ms. I eat them.

I want ice cream. I indulge myself.

Is this a look at my mortality? The need to have what I want before I die?

I can't help it. I just want and so I do. I don't restrain myself anymore. I did go to the gym though—three times this week! And it did elevate my mood.

Loneliness

Daniel just left. Already I feel lonely.

My textbooks are before me, but I don't really care anymore. What's the point? I'm going to lose my breast and all my hair. I would rather be researching "my disease" than studying anyway. My cancer book is at my feet. The fish swim in need of water and the cat is out of the room. Alex is sick today, so I can't rely on him to talk and fill the void. I want someone with me all the time. Maybe I'm very demanding? And now I'm back to being alone.

Here comes the cat! I love her, and I can play with her! Oh, and there she goes . . .

Psych 101

I'm seeing a therapist. She helps me think through ideas and identify things that may not be obvious to me. I don't think there's anything wrong with that. Is there still a stereotype against it? I'm just a normal human being with good moods and bad, ups and downs. Maybe I need medication to get me through? Sometimes you just need to talk to someone who's not your mother, a husband, a boyfriend, a friend before you say something so big that you can never take it back.

Change

Everyone keeps telling me how this is going to change my life. How I'm going to feel differently about the world, notice the colors, smell the flowers more than I do now or ever have. But I don't see it. It's not going to change me. I will still have the same bills, the same apartment, the same few, close friends. Nothing's going to change except for my breast and my hair.

I told this to a friend also suffering from breast cancer, and she said, "Maybe it won't be so dramatic, but still things will change. Maybe it will be your eating habits and how you cook your food."

OK, maybe I can see that happening.

Chapter 2 Tips

Meditative breathing

When you're going through testing, the unknown and the waiting are even worse than *some* of the tests.

It helps to do meditative breathing, known as circle, or box, breathing, while you're waiting. Continue until you feel a little more relaxed.

1. Inhale slowly through your nose while you count to four.
2. Hold for four.
3. Exhale through your mouth for four.
4. Hold for four.

With each inhale, imagine white healing light coming in; during each exhale, imagine black smoke exiting, taking all the toxins out.

Asking questions

Not wanting to rock the boat or bother my surgeon, nurse, or PA, I kept questions to myself. But it's my job to ask the important questions. Questions need to be asked and answered, so it's important to empower yourself to ask even the little questions. *I hear the nurses cursing me right now.* Yes, nurses may have to repeat the answers to every patient, but each patient deserves to know the answers and has a right and a need to know them. That way, you can determine if you are confident in your surgeon and secure you will be taken care of when you need it most.

Questions to ask the general surgeon:

-Is my cancer invasive or non-invasive?

-What stage and grade are my cancer cells and what might be determined after surgery that is not showing in the images and biopsy(s)?

-How likely is this to spread or come back?

-Should I have genetic testing done? What type? How long will the results take? Do we need to wait on surgery for the results? How will treatment vary depending upon the results? Will insurance cover genetic testing? How expensive is it?

-What are my options now that I am diagnosed? Do you recommend a lumpectomy, mastectomy, or double?

-How many of these surgeries have you done?

-How do these surgeries differ in follow-up and maintaining a cancer-free status?

-What types of future assessments will there be: self-exams, clinical exams, scans?

-What is the risk of recurrence with this surgery? How can the risk be lowered?

-What comes first, chemo or surgery, and why?

-Do I have to have this surgery now or can I wait?

-Are you in my insurance network? What will my expenses be if you're not?

-What will the treatment be after surgery?

-When does reconstruction start? What plastic surgeons do you work with?

-What are the survival rates?

Things families, friends, and caregivers can do

-Offer to go to an appointment with the patient and take notes. In the moment, they may feel too overwhelming to do this themselves.

-Offer to be a relay person. It's too intense to have to go over and update everyone on the same details. Offer to be the go-to person. Another option is to sign up for Caring Bridge, a website that displays this type of information for the patient so it only needs to be written once and concerning individuals can go there for updates. You can be the go-to person to input the information.

-Invite the patient for coffee, or dinner, even if you don't know what to say. Sometimes they just want company.

-Send them letters—many sites on the internet have appropriate cards if you don't know what to say.

-*With kids* do a seated meditation together. Sit on the floor, or in chairs if you can't tolerate the floor. Play a guided meditation, which can be found in the app store, iTunes, the internet, or YouTube. Practice together the breathing method described in this section. Exaggerate a big inhale with arm movements coming up from below the belly to the sky and then exhale pushing them down. This can be done standing as well. Repeat.

-Go for a walk or to the gym with them.

September–Mid-November

Chapter 3—Tests Unlike Those in School and Operation #1

I'm the epitome of a perpetual student. I'm constantly taking classes, enrolled in one school or another, but these tests were not ones I signed up for. Every week another one is scheduled and each successive one reveals more and more of the whole picture. The lumpectomy versus mastectomy question became one I didn't answer; my pathology did.

Often provoking pain, the majority of the experiences are new for me so they were interesting, to say the least. I rely on writing down my experiences as one method to escape.

Going to the Beach

It's supposed to rain—20 percent chance—and only be in the 70s, but we decide to go anyway. I need to get away before everything else begins.

A day at the beach. A day to feel *free*. Hearing the sound of the sea, floating in the salty water, diving through the crashing waves, I soak it all up. The wind gently blows my hair and I bury my toes in the sand as I lie on a towel, lathered up with suntan lotion, at the shore.

The weather holds and the temperature is perfect. It's all I imagined. I know I'm not supposed to be worshipping the sun, so we don't stay out too long.

I feel the heat in my body going home and wonder, "Is this what radiation feels like?"

I return home and take a luscious shower, still dreaming of my wonderful escape.

Getting My Menses

I got my period.

Now, it's *ten days* and counting until my MRI.

Genetics—The Need to Know

Would I be better off if I didn't know? Do I want the answer? Can I face the answer?

Different people have different reasons for needing to know ... family history, doctor recommendations, etc. I need to know because I don't want to have to go through this again. Preventative maintenance means if I have the BRCA1 or BRCA2 gene, I'll probably have to remove my ovaries as well as both breasts. As much as part of the whole genetics thing frightens me, if it comes back telling me I need to take out my ovaries, then so be it. I'll deal with that too.

So, the genetic counselor hands me a tube and I swoosh and swish liquid around in my mouth and spit it into the tube. Done. But I know my insurance won't cover it so eventually it'll be a small fortune I need to find the funds for. This apparently is par for the course in this whole breast cancer journey.

Giving Them Away for Free

I don't feel like going to sleep tonight. Today, I found out my surgery date. When I got off the phone, the silence enveloped me. There was nothing to say. There it was. Finally. The date. Lumpectomy. Still don't know what to say or do about it. It's just there hanging around in the air. Words, numbers, not making any sense.

They'll send me information. I can call if I have any questions.

How do I get outta this? I'm petrified, like a shiny piece of wood. Maybe I should go line up some crystals, get some reiki done. Maybe it's too late?

Everyone says I'll be fine—chopping off my breast is no big deal. Well, maybe I just don't want to simply give them away.

Give up the fight. Just give it up.

This isn't a battle here; I'm simply allowing myself to be healed. I'm beating the cancer, destroying the gremlin who has decided to play house and eat me up from the inside. Well, I found him, and as scared as I am, soon he'll be gone. I'll go back to my life a changed woman. One who had to face some difficult choices but survived. Different and yet the same. A dichotomy.

I'm thinking about organizing my life: what I want to do, who I want to see.

I can't really imagine. I just have to wait and see.

A "Cookie"

It's a beautiful fall day—even though it's not technically autumn yet. A clear blue sky radiates warmth while white billowy clouds cool the body. There are less than thirty days now until my surgery.

I had my clearance appointment with my primary care doctor today. My doctor had a student with her; he was a sweet young man who wore a bowtie. She asked if he could feel my lump because he had never had that experience before. Afterward, he went out of his way to find me an article related to my schoolwork.

I am home now, and I just stare into my cat's golden eyes for an eternity except that tears well up and sound comes out of my mouth scaring her away. I need to be studying now, but what's the use? Nothing has been sticking these past couple of weeks. Or has it even been months? I can no longer tell. "Please don't make me go to school tonight," I pray. Maybe this situation actually is starting to affect me.

Tomorrow I'll do blood work and now added to the "list" is a chest x-ray, followed by an appointment to go over results.

My baby jumps up on my lap purring. A little slice of heaven. A "cookie," Alex would say. A sweet moment to hold on to and cherish, like the cherry on top of an ice cream sundae.

Snake Veins

I'm getting blood work done. The woman can't find my vein.

She asks, "Do your veins move?"

What? Are they like snakes? Not that I know of and most phlebotomists have no problem finding them, but I decide not to be rude and merely reply, "I don't know."

She takes a child's needle and uses the other arm.

DCIS—Ductal Carcinoma in Situ

My aunt had DCIS: ductal carcinoma in situ, a non-invasive breast cancer. I never knew this. She tells me they gave her a biopsy, and it was so small it all came out then. They followed her with mammograms every six months, but then they went back to once a year with no problems since. She says she has a little scar, but it doesn't bother her that much. I'm quite concerned about what my scar will look like, but she says, "They make very little incisions now."

Deep Space Nine MRI

The setup of the MRI machine is strange, but I guess serves a purpose. I'm lying on my belly with my arms reaching forward like superman with a narrow sternum bar supporting my chest. My breasts hang down and are supported slightly by two side panels or flaps.

I was told it would be loud, so I'm prepared. They put headphones on me and send me in. The music comes on, and I think it's too loud. I think of saying something, but quickly the knocking sounds start and drown out the music. Now, I get the point.

The noise is really loud.

The sounds are so foreign. I think about a space station like I've seen in the movies. These must be the massive noises that occur in deep space. It's very interesting; this isn't so bad.

But the noise is really loud.

At one point there is such a large boom that it feels like the sternum bar drops. I wonder if I should tell them by squeezing the emergency ball they placed in my hand before the test started, but I know if I squeeze it, they will have to start the test again. I don't want that. I decide to stay as still as possible and wait until the test ends. After all, they should be able to tell if the machine broke.

The noise is really loud.

I try to meditate to drown out the noise, but I am being so thoroughly bombarded with sound I can't truly think what is happening. I start praying to God. One girl I know had told me she made up rap songs during hers to get through.

The noise is really loud.

A few times the sound frequency makes me cry, and I mean cry. But all I can think is *stop crying, you have to stay still, or you'll have to retake the test from the beginning!* It's hard to contain myself, so I pray more. I pray to make this all go away and to please wake me up from this extraterrestrial dream.

The noise is really loud.

Then suddenly, it's over. And the "dropped bar" turns out to have been a vibration, so it was good I hadn't squeezed the ball.

The noise was so loud.

The Cost of Plastic Surgery

I'm starting to get nervous. It's so small; why does it have to come out? Cutting open my chest and engulfing the mass with a good margin to be extra safe—is it all necessary? What if they do it and don't get enough? Or, worse yet, what if they get too much and my breast has a divot the size of a miniature state of Connecticut? OK, so I'm being a little extreme, I realize that, but that doesn't stop the tears in my eyes and the massive sadness that wells up in my heart.

Why me? Breast cancer is the number one cancer in women: it's not just me. But with so many sufferers, why can't we figure out how to prevent this? Not just to "cure" it, but to make it go away? Why do we have to suffer and have our breasts cut open? A main part of our femininity is being debased. Oh, but then we can have plastic surgery and "get the breasts we've always wanted." Yes, maybe, but at what cost?

To Surgery or Not to Surgery

Twenty-three days. Who's counting?

I don't want to have this surgery. I've never had surgery except for having my wisdom teeth out, *twice*. Two and two because I was scared to do them at the same time and only two were impacted the first time anyway.

People are telling me about holistic cures and alternatives to surgery. Two friends were cured. Another went from stage 4 to stage 1. On the other hand, a sister's husband's cousin, wow that's a mouthful, died because she didn't take care of her cancer. Emails, phone calls, and office coworkers all telling me different stories.

Please, just go away!

This time I have to do it my way, and right now, though I don't want it, my way means surgery. I'm still petrified, but there's no other way I can see. Maybe if I was older, maybe if I was in remission and having breast cancer for the second time, but for right now the holistic cleansing route won't work. It's just not going to happen; I have to take the traditional medicine route.

I am, however, scheduled to see a nutritionist. One that will help me with cancer-related eating and creating a meal plan to follow. Here the goal will be to prevent future cancer from developing. It may work. We will see if I can live my life that way and truly change. Maybe I'll even start cooking and using my pristine, probably ten-years-old, barely broken in pots and pans!

Choosing a Nutritionist

Everyone continues to tell me I need to eat right and need a nutritionist. I must change my diet or at least eat more foods that prevent cancer and avoid ones that cause it. The nutritionist I had in mind won't help me plan my meals. This is what I really need. I hesitate, but find another one.

This one tells me I should work with her because she knows everything about cancer. I believe her; is that crazy? How can she know *everything* about cancer nutrition? I decide to trust her and go for it.

A Whole New Life—A Whole New Me

What would I eat if I could eat anything? Chocolate cake? Ice cream? Tiramisu? Cheese?

What would I eat if I could eat anything, *but* it had to be nutritious?

I often eat out, taking leftovers home for the next day, which I love! I don't eat at fast food restaurants per se, but I eat at Panera, Chinese takeout, and sushi places.

It's hard to think of changing my diet. Won't healthier food cost more and take longer to prepare? Am I ready for that? That's an entire lifestyle change.

And what if I have to throw out my entire kitchen and learn how to actually cook, which friends confirm will take longer if I'm being healthy?

I have to look into the future here. How much better will it be? I'll have my kitchen more organized and my meals will be more fulfilling. Keep your focus there, Karen. Keep focusing there.

Making Room

I'm tired.

I go to the farmers' market to buy fresh food. It's not even a mile, but for some reason, today it seems so far away. Returning home, I clean out my entire fridge.

I decide not to tackle the freezer yet.

Looking at the pantry I think, *Soon will be your turn, my friend. I'm definitely not starting now.*

I had a normal day, and yet I'm exhausted—and I haven't even had the surgery yet.

My Breast's Death

I cry. I cry a lot today. My MRI results came back yesterday. The right breast is clear, but they want to sonogram the left again to look at another spot. I guess I should be happy—the right one is good. But I'm not.

My friend Daniel looked up lumpectomies online, and he told me they all left deformities. My breasts are going to be uneven and deformed. How will I look at them every day in the mirror? How will I ever forget I've had breast cancer? How will I be able to accept what was once beautiful will now be, at best, a plastic surgery job?

I'm a natural person, not wanting anything "artificial" inside me. Plus, doesn't it need to be maintained? Don't you have to get an implant refilled or replaced every few years?

What happens when I show myself to my love? How will he react? Will I have to keep my top on with one side of by bra stuffed?

I can imagine getting intimate, going slowly, then it comes to the big reveal . . . I can't continue the thought. It's too much. Having one breast on the right side and nothing on the left—a flat surface—or a breast that is deformed, is uneven, and has divots and pocks . . . or some fake thing, an implant or reconstruction of some sort. The idea is mortifying. It might as well be the Grand Canyon in there.

My heart breaks.

Which is better—a hole or having a small, scary lump? Maybe I should just keep the lump.

Heading Down

I lie in bed all day today.

I know there is something wrong when I don't even get up for my mom.

Shut Down

I don't want to talk anymore. No more questions. No more answers. I'm done. Finito. That's it. Sayonara, dude. Clear enough?

I had another sonogram today. My doctor tells me I will need two further biopsies. I don't like biopsies. Check please? I'm outta here.

I can't blame her though; she's just doing her job to make sure everything is known before we go into the surgery room in two weeks. Now, I'm scheduled for an MRI on Tuesday *with* a biopsy. This has been the never-ending saga of tests. Ever since I was diagnosed, I've had at least one test every week. Why is this taking so long? I want it out, now. Is that really too much to ask?

The Panel of Judges

Today I found out I am not a mutant from Mars. I guess it's easy for me to joke about the gene test when I just found out I don't have the genetic mutation people like me need to worry about—the one that leads to ovarian cancer. Maybe it's a way of releasing the stress and worry since I now know my results are negative. Of course, I could still get ovarian cancer spontaneously, but my genes don't predict it. I think of friends with positive results who have had to face whether they should remove both breasts *and* their ovaries, and maybe even their entire uterus, in order to prevent further possible cancer; it's not an easy thing to face, I imagine. It wouldn't really be my choice, though—I would go with my doctor's recommendation. As hard as it would be, I would opt to take everything out if my doctor instructed me to do so. Then, I wouldn't have to worry every single day: *Is this pain I'm feeling normal? Have I developed it yet? Do I need to see my doctor?* Or the big one: *Do I have cancer again?*

Some pains, I resolve, are easier to manage than others.

The Plot Thickens

OK, so, you knew this title was coming, but the plot really did just get that much more intense.

I call my doctor's office. My nurse answers the phone—I know her voice by heart now—and she says we're going to go ahead with the biopsy assisted MRI and see the results before we schedule the stereotactic biopsy. We're looking at two additional areas where there are calcium deposits, and if one is a tumor, we'll have to remove the entire breast.

I knew this was coming so I was prepared. *Right?* Wrong! No one is. So genetics had ruled out the double mastectomy, and we went back to the lumpectomy and the resulting divot and scars. Now, we're potentially back to the mastectomy again because I have more than one area with a tumor. Prepared? Not at all.

The flood comes in. How could this happen to me? Why did I get cancer? What did I do wrong in my life to deserve this?

Cold Feet

Saturday is officially the start of autumn. I don't know why, but the weather report almost moved me to tears. I take a deep gulp in. Maybe it's the passage of time? These past few months have felt like half a year at least. And then these upcoming ones that I will lose to cancer treatments, how long will they last?

It's already cooler, and I feel like the cells in my body are cold too. Cells circulate, move slowly, and affect my hands and feet. But what does this have to do with breast cancer? Maybe nothing. Maybe it reminds me of the frailty of life. Plants die, animals die, I could die at any moment. Anyone could. But the cancer cells inside me defy the rules of nature by "forgetting how to die"; instead, they only know how to continuously replicate.

Today, we had a bad storm with tornado warnings in areas where they've never been before. Are we doing to our bodies what we're doing to the Earth? In our race for technology, what effects can't be assessed for multiple generations to come? Should we be worried about the effects to our bodies by our actions? And why is breast cancer being diagnosed so much more frequently in younger and younger women?

I am one of them, I think. This brings a gulp to my throat.

I don't want to die.

They're Better Than They Were Before

I was told that one phrase would be repeated and repeated and repeated so much I would no longer be able to stand hearing it: "They're better than they were before."

All these women claim they're so happy now, post-mastectomy, because their breasts are more beautiful, more equal in size, more perky. Come on! I like my breasts just as they are. Maybe they're not perfect, but they're mine. They're original as God intended. They're natural, and I'm a natural person. I don't want plastic inside me filled with gel or saline. Is that really what people want and love? Apparently, the consensus is yes.

Don't Want To

I don't want to have surgery. I understand that I have to, but I don't want to. I'm afraid. Afraid of them cutting me open. Afraid of what my breast will look like when they're done. Afraid of the pain and mental and physical anguish.

One friend said it took her seven weeks to recover, granted she had a double mastectomy, but I only have one week off from school. Plus, I'll have to wear "drains"—whatever those really are. I guess I'll find out soon.

Not wanting to do things pervades my life although once I get started with it, with whatever, I'm fine. In fact, I usually enjoy whatever I'm doing. I hope, in a weird way, this will be the same: my not wanting to do it will morph into an experience I've never had. I'll "learn" from it. I can't feel what this future pain is like so right now this future pain doesn't hurt so much. But, still, the fear of everything is overwhelming.

Tests Unlike Those in School and Operation #1

Prayers and Why We Suffer

I do wrong things in my life but am really a good person overall. I have feelings; I have cares. There are responsibilities and obligations I need to attend to. And, then, there it comes: cancer. It's such a feared word. No one wants it. No one wants to hear about it, know about it, or worse yet, be near anyone who's got it. Forget about having it.

My friend's wife had her annual mammogram today. There was a shadow. He asks me to pray for her, to pray she doesn't have breast cancer *like me*. I sincerely pray she doesn't.

Cancer. Yuck! It changes lives. I don't want to go through this so why would she? But now it's got me thinking: Do I deserve this? If I were closer to God would He have protected me? Is there a reason I have this death sentence? Everything happens for a reason? Or then there's the idea of *perseverance*—difficulties strengthen our faith.

Little Things

"Little steps can add up to great things," I say.

I'm at my gym and they are selling several breast cancer items. I buy a pink bracelet that says: Live well, Love much, Laugh often.

I will wear it every day.

Waiting

Waiting is the hardest part.

Misplaced Laughter

I'm in class and, apparently, what my professor just said was the most hysterical thing in the world. I'm laughing so hard, but it doesn't last. Soon, my laughter turns into tears and my sobbing forces me to get up and run out of the room.

My teacher comes after me shortly thereafter, "You know you have to go through with this," he says.

"With what?" I say, completely lost in my tears. "Go through with what?"

"The surgery," he replies. "You're very stressed out, but you have to do it. There's no other option."

My tears dry up as I stand there. In my heart, I know he's right.

Shifting Priorities and Clearing the Clutter

The radio changes my mood. All the music is about love or a situation that can change. Why do I have to be such a defect? My situation will never go away. Yes, I'll get the cancer out; I will be "cured," but it will still be with me. I'll always have the scars both physically and mentally.

I just want to be normal for once. Oh, to be like everyone else. I guess no one really is "normal," though. In college I had a purple car sticker that read in big white letters: Why Be Normal? I know everyone has problems and their own way of feeling and being. I guess, my way is to cry, write, talk to my friends, sigh, take a deep breath, and then go for a walk or sometimes to the gym. That's what I do. It would be so much nicer to look forward to a vacation on a cruise ship rather than a surgery and recovery at home.

Maybe, I need to shift my mindset? Maybe, I need to rearrange my bathroom to look like a spa and make my living room and bedroom into serene rooms of rest and peace? Could my kitchen be transformed into an inviting space for cooking with bright lights and large, clear counters? Maybe. Just maybe, it might help.

It's hard for me to let go, though. After my dad died of cancer I tried to in essence become my dad rather than be true to myself. This continued into my adulthood. It affected who I was and where my career path led. After he died my mom struggled with finances and my perception was that things would be taken away if I didn't do what I was told . . . I always felt I had to pinch my pennies. Now I keep things because they offer me comfort. If I keep them, I have them; I possess them; they're mine. I save paperwork so I have it to look at again in the future. My mind thinks, I might need, or want it, and if I get rid of it, I'll have to buy it again. Here the money comes into play. Mind you, this doesn't mean I'm a hoarder; I just have a lot of stuff. This affects relationships as well. With boyfriends, I tend to stay with them when the relationship has already run its course. Then I ruminate about them way past the time it would be healthier to move on. But facing this medical diagnosis, it may be time to change these habits and clear myself of the physical and internal clutter.

I decide to start clearing the clutter by working in my bedroom, and I open my closet doors. So much clothing hangs before me and much of it I never wear. I search through the items and take out a floral skirt. Do I absolutely love it? No. Have I worn it in the past year? Yes, but only once. I place it on my bed and decide this is the first step in clearing my clutter. I come across a sleeveless green top that I haven't worn. My mind says, *But I like it*. But I haven't worn it so I take it out too. I begin to feel more confident about taking another item out and feel peace in taking some control of my otherwise chaotic situation.

Losing Friends

I have a friend who has been so supportive so far in this whole process. He has come to appointments with me–picking up bagels no matter what time of day. But today I somewhat backed away. Everything just became too much. Recent fun dinners had become argumentative and now normal questions turned invasive. The friendship started to shake. This is not a time to be giving up friends, I thought, and I have a long road ahead. Still, something had to be done.

He and I spoke and agreed on the problems. We didn't exactly determine a resolution.

So much is changing right now; I need some stability in my life, not fights.

The Double Whammy

Tomorrow is a double whammy. An MRI *with* a biopsy in *two* places. My right breast may be fine, but my left is potentially very messed up. This test may then lead to another biopsy. All within one and a half weeks of my surgery, no wonder I'm not feeling so well!

Sleeping Away the Dream—The MRI-Guided Breast Biopsy

Yesterday, I had an MRI-guided breast biopsy. Today, I just want to stay in bed. I feel violated by having things inserted into me in ways that bring pain with nothing I can do about it but stay perfectly still like I'm told.

It started with the typical superman position—on my belly with my arms stretched out straight above my head. They had me move down a bit so my face was only supported by my cheek on a narrow bar and my breast fell through the hole in the table. After that they clamped down my breast so it wouldn't move—this part actually was not that painful. They kept asking me to straighten my arms more as if I really were flying. My arms were not supported at all, and I didn't foresee how painful this would become.

They sent me into the tube and completed the first round of images, both without and with dyes. My radiologist informed me that the two areas of calcifications were still there, so they were going to proceed as planned and biopsy both areas.

Additional MRIs were performed marking the spots, but the worst part was when they started to put the needles in. My radiologist started injecting lidocaine to numb the breast. "A little pinch," she said when the needle went in and then, "some pressure," as it continued in. This was repeated several times. Then they put needles in to mark the areas in question, left them in, and sent me back inside the tube to check the accuracy of the spots.

I felt like a pig being basted and spun with acupuncture needles sticking out. And my arms were starting to hurt, but there was nothing I could do.

I then found out the biopsy was next. It hadn't even started yet! They cleaned out the holes with water and the sound of the machine was like a mini drill spinning away. I'm not even certain when the actual biopsy began but a nurse was standing by my side holding my hand. I said "ouch" several times, which was an understatement, and she said, "You have the littlest 'ouch.'" In some bizarre way that made me feel a little better. I finally told them my arms were in a lot of pain and about to fall off, and the nurse bent them and moved them a little, which did make a difference.

I went back in the tunnel, had a few more MRIs, and then they inserted clips to mark the biopsy locations. They lowered the table. Finally, it was done.

I gingerly got up and one of the nurses came over and put pressure on the spots to stop the bleeding. She gave me an ice pack to continue the pressure. It sounds so black and white, so simple, but it wasn't. And, then, I learned it *wasn't* over.

I got dressed and was sent to the breast center for some mammograms. I feared the additional pain as I traveled to another part of the hospital. When I disrobed to don the white "mammogram robe," which maybe is given to women to make them feel like they're at the spa, I found blood on my shirt. Realizing I was still bleeding, I knew the white robe would soon be red too. I asked for assistance and was given another ice pack and a face cloth. I held the ice pack and face cloth over the incision sites and waited.

The mammogram wasn't what I expected. She only needed to take three images. But since I was still bleeding, a puddle of blood was left on the machine after each picture, so the tech had to clean up in between each image. Then she bandaged me up and sent me back to the waiting room.

Shortly, thereafter, they told me I was done.

I spoke to my radiology nurse about the implications of these tests and was told if either location was cancerous, I would have a mastectomy. She gave me the business card of a plastic surgeon they work with and informed me I could look on the doctor's website at photos of her reconstruction work. I expressed my concern that one breast would be perky while the other was droopy. She mentioned that the law now states that insurance companies are required to cover all future reconstructions. I still wasn't certain.

"You'll know what to do," she said.

So, today I've spent half the day in bed. Maybe, I think, if I pretend to be asleep this dream will go away.

The Queen and Her Princess

I let myself fall asleep in my armchair last night. Maybe it was the security of it. It's the first piece of furniture I've ever owned, and it has comforted me on many a night. It doesn't want anything from me. It just sits there waiting for me to appreciate it by sitting down. It's my queen chair. The queen and her matching princess ottoman are covered in beige fabric with a floral pattern in tans, browns, and reds. It has a matching pillow to boot! I once went to sell it to my fashion-forward friend Kyra but never did. If she wanted it, it must be in vogue! Now, in reflecting back, I'm glad I never sold it.

The Final Diagnosis

On Tuesday, I had my MRI assisted biopsy. Today, three days later, I receive the results. I have a second spot in my left breast, a pre-cancerous in situ ductal carcinoma. Though not as bad as my invasive ductal carcinoma, my nurse told me, "We treat it the same." This means I'll have a mastectomy, not a lumpectomy. A bigger surgery and plastic reconstruction will be involved. My surgery date needs to be changed, and next Tuesday I will consult with my doctor to pin down more of the details. My mom was scheduled to fly in for the lumpectomy so now her flights will need to be rebooked. And everything I had planned for the next week needs to be rearranged.

The one positive is that they caught this now. I can only imagine how devastated I would be if I had had the lumpectomy next week and then found out a year later I had another lump.

There's more I need to say:

Am I angry? *Yes.*

Am I crying? *No.*

Do I want to curl up in my bed and hide within the fur of my cat? *You bet!*

But I'll get through this too. Somehow, I will. I need to keep reminding myself of that.

Invasive Ductal Carcinoma

My friend's wife was just diagnosed with invasive ductal carcinoma, just like me except her tumor is smaller and she is having hers removed almost immediately. It makes me really sad, maybe even mad at the same time, that this disease is so prevalent. So many women, and some men, are plagued by it. Currently the statistic from the American Cancer Society is one woman out of every eight will get it at some time in their lifetime. It's so invasive, pun intended, destroying something so primal to a female's body. Breasts, a symbol of femininity, being cut open or completely taken off, invading and leaving marks, physically and emotionally, which never completely go away.

They will check her lymph nodes during the surgery. It's hard for him to know how to act, what to do. My friend feels he needs to be strong for her and not show his fears—so he hides them behind closed doors. But maybe she needs to see his fears too, to be comforted in tears together. I found out there are books specifically for spouses of women with breast cancer—how to help and what not to do. I told him maybe he can simply ask her how he can help. Perhaps, offer to clean the house and do some grocery shopping or cooking. Just doing these simple tasks will take a little responsibility off her shoulders.

How would I feel? I think his tears would be OK, showing his honest feelings and fears. I would need brave and supportive moments too, especially when I'm being prepped for surgery and being rolled away. At that moment, it might be just as hard, if not harder, for him as she'll be in a sort of pre-surgery shock and he'll be watching her head into surgery. I think sincerity is expected; this is his life partner so feelings and reactions shouldn't be falsified.

I think of all the women who have had to go through, and will go through what we have. Yet I haven't even gone through it. Maybe the journey is worse than the actual mastectomy? I know breast cancer is considered "curable," but I don't know, it's Cancer with a capital "C." Somehow putting it behind "breast" makes it seem less severe. All I know is I'll never be the same knowing I've had it, seeing the visible scar, and feeling the gel implant every day for the rest of my life. I will become more used to it as time goes by, but I think I'll always fear someday the big bad "C"—in some form—will come back.

The Fear of Solitude

In a few weeks, I'll have no one. My friend who has been taking me to all of my appointments is moving to "the City" (New York), and my family will only be here for two weeks. After that I'll have to make it to my surgeon's office for whatever treatments they determine and to my plastic surgeon's appointments on my own. They will probably say I can't exercise and I will not be able to lift heavy grocery bags. I'll also need to get to the supermarket. And I don't know how I will be feeling. What will hurt? And why does it take so long to recover?

Breaking Through to Tomorrow

Get out, get out, get out, get out! Get out of my body! Get out, get out, get out of my head! I don't want this thing, this infection, in my body anymore or these thoughts inside my head. *Get out already*! Enough is enough; no more waiting, not one more day, for this surgery. I'm afraid of it, and I'm afraid my reconstructed breast will be lumpy.

Aaaaaggghhhhh! I want to scream!

I want to throw my cell phone on the floor and then cry when it's all shattered in pieces.

Maybe I need to break down. To not be strong anymore and be alone, all alone. *Everyone, go away!* Leave me alone to wallow in my misery and suffer through my own pain.

But isolating is not the answer, and I'm rational enough to know that.

I saw the nutritionist, and she gave me a whole list of things to do for my body. I started doing them and felt good. Then, a classmate ate chips right in front of me and I felt influenced to eat them too. Afterward, I no longer felt good.

Last night I had two margaritas, which were perfect, but then again, afterward . . .

Right now, I don't feel very good. It seems like I'm having a meltdown because I can't take this anymore. It comes down to my being scared, and on top of everything, I spent too much money today. Maybe I should just go to bed because I can't deal with anything negative right now. Tomorrow, I'll get some exercise. Tomorrow, I'll feel better than today.

One of Those Days

I'm crying. Today was supposed to be my surgery—a lumpectomy—which is a day visit to the hospital. I'd almost be home by now. I wouldn't know the results of the lymph node dissection, but I would be cancer free. There would still be radiation, but the cancer would be gone. Until now I hadn't realized how significant being cancer free would be to me. Now, I don't know when my mastectomy will be and again the game has stepped up a notch. Two sites with cancer needing to be removed, then an expander, followed by an implant. It's all too grotesque for words, and yet I know others with breast cancer have it far worse. And add to that my kitty threw up last night and now keeps staring at her poopy box as if her diarrhea is about to explode again. I guess it's just one of those days.

The Gorgeous Turquoise Sea

My new surgery date is now one month away. That seems so long, considering I was diagnosed three months ago. My mom has offered me a week in Aruba before I have the surgery, and I can't figure out why I'm not completely thrilled. Maybe it's knowing that this will be the last time I'll be at the beach in my natural form with my natural breast. I'll have an artificial breast after this trip, and it's not a change I'm choosing to make.

Lying on the beach, will I be relaxed or thinking, twenty-six more days? Will I be thinking, Last licks there, Molly? Maybe, I'll just be a little remorseful. Or maybe, I'll be fine.

I am looking forward to going. I love the beach, and it will be nice to get away, take my mind off things, soak up some warm sun, and swim in the gorgeous turquoise, blue sea. I know I'll try not to get too much sun because I don't want to get skin cancer like my friend. When I was a little girl, I once got a blister the whole length of my forearm on my right arm from too much sun. Now, I make sure to use enough sunblock and don't stay out in the sun too long.

1:04 A.M.

I'm wearing a hole in my carpet as I walk in circles during an anxiety attack. All the stress I've been under has gotten to me. I tried to relax by calling a friend whom I haven't spoken to in a long time. No luck, as she tells me she may be getting a divorce. My other friend I wish to speak with is not available since she died in a car crash earlier this year. As a third attempt, I reach out to my best friend, who lives in Canada, and he is there for me. I cry to him and he soothes me.

I raise my voice.

He listens.

Irrationally, I express my need to punch the shit out of something just so it too will feel my pain. We rationalize even that wouldn't be the same as what I'm going through.

Now, hours later, I can't sleep. I haven't been able to these past few nights. It's partly because I don't want to sleep and partly due to anxiety. I don't want tomorrow to come, and yet I sure as hell don't want to stay in today. I think, why can't I jump ahead one year? Then all this crap would be over. My new boob would be installed and ready to go.

Oh, dreams, how wonderful they can sometimes be.

I hold up my middle finger to God for putting me in this position. Maybe it's not his fault and he didn't do anything, but still I need someone to blame.

My cat sits beside me licking herself clean. If only I had it so good.

The Reality in My Dreams

Aaagggghhhhh! I'm lying in my recovery room bed and my breast is gone.

Oooowwwwww! I'm lying in my recovery room bed, and I lean over on my left arm and remnant breast.

Pain.

Then I wake up.

I overslept a doctor's appointment this morning. I had an anxiety attack, took an anti-anxiety pill, and then didn't wake up.

Today, I speak to my plastic surgeon's office. They still don't have clearance from my insurance company and the surgery is less than three weeks away. Am I going to have to find a new plastic surgeon now? Panic rushes through my mind. I've waited so long for this surgery; I can't have anything jeopardize it now.

The Wizard and Her Wand

Today I meet with my plastic surgeon for the second time.

After checking in, I go to speak with the woman in charge of billing. I need to know if my insurance company has cleared me since my surgery is only one week away. She isn't there, so I pose my question to the woman who is, and to my embarrassment my plastic surgeon turns around and says I shouldn't worry. To my surprise, her office is right off the billing area.

"But she'll be here in about ten minutes if you want to wait," my surgeon says.

I go back to the waiting room and sit down. Very shortly afterward I am brought into the examination room. As I wait and fill out indemnity papers stating I am aware of the potential risks of the surgery, I begin to feel very unstable. My doctor comes in to talk to me and I start crying.

"Why are you crying?" she asks. All I can come up with is that I'm scared. She says I have nothing to worry about. "Everything will be fine," she says. She explains that yes, I will have pain, but otherwise I will be fine.

Her PA comes in next to take the pictures I consented to.

Then, my doctor returns to examine my breasts. It is the fastest exam I think I've ever had! Not in a bad way, though. She is looking to see what size expander I need. She confirms I am just reconstructing the left breast and not changing the right. Then she says, "Do you know your right breast is larger than your left?" Apparently, breasts usually are not the same size.

I laugh, "No. I guess I'm having an enlargement then!"

On the way out I stop in again with billing and am told that my clearance just came through. I take a copy for safe keeping.

One Lump or Two?

The reconstruction pictures on the internet look lumpy. I call my breast plastic surgeon and I'm told I'm wrong. My reinterpretation: they just look weird. They don't look natural, and I want mine to look the way they are. Am I being unreasonable?

Every breast is different. I guess it's even irregular for a woman to have two breasts that are the same size. However, despite my doctor telling me mine were not the same size, they looked like they were to me. I never noticed a difference. No one ever told me they were different. That is until now.

Rose's Story of Success

At the hair salon, I am introduced to Rose, a seven-year survivor of breast cancer. Bless her heart. She tells me about going through radiation and chemo. For radiation, she went every day and had to stand in a mold with her arm and hand up, and for chemo, she went every other week. The loss of hair, she says, "allows you to dress up: wear different wigs, pretty hats, and earrings." She goes on, "There are two kinds of people—those who let cancer overcome them and those who push through it. You have to do it! Don't let it get you down! You can beat it!" She explains doctors can't use the word "cured," even though breast cancer is thought of as a "curable" cancer. She tells me about a woman she knew who broke down in tears when her doctor couldn't tell her this.

Rose is a strong woman. Though she had times when she broke down, she made it. She arranged for her radiation to be at lunchtime so she could keep working and her coworkers merely thought she was out to lunch. Her family responsibilities were met as well, taking care of her grandchild. She didn't let cancer beat her.

What did I learn? Fight it! Be strong! Attack! Use my attitude to get through and never succumb!

It was nice to meet her—to know it can be done and that I too will survive. She presented a little rainbow in the midst of a darkened sky.

Swimming in the Panama Canal

I'm in Panama, and even here, pink symbols decorate the terminal entrance and are pinned on traveler's chests. It's good to know that worldwide recognition and efforts to eradicate this disease exist. And as sad as it may make me feel that the problem persists everywhere, I take comfort in knowing that I'm not alone.

Facing a Brick Wall

Today in Aruba, I take a tour with ABC Tours. It's fantastic. Our guide leads us around the island with energy and knowledge and genuine Aruban charm. "Anna" becomes my pseudonym for the day since my mom scheduled the tour for me and her name was on the list. For whatever reason, I never correct anyone.

We stop at the Alto Vista Chapel. It has large dark brown wooden doors, and it overlooks the beautiful Caribbean blue sea that I imagine Enya sings about. It was built in 1750 and is still in use today for Catholic services on Tuesdays. Inside the church, I buy a candle. It may be sacrilegious because I'm not Catholic, but I do it anyway. I light it and make a "wish." I don't know if it's like birthdays in that you're not allowed to share your prayer for fear it won't come true, but mine, you can bet, has something to do with my breast cancer. When I leave the church, I feel an immediate shift in my mood.

The rest of the day includes many stops, but I especially enjoy the two swimming and snorkeling opportunities. Floating in the warm sea, I see beautiful fish below and feel like my real life has been left way far away in the abyss. This tour is truly what I need for my mind to escape and is worth every penny.

When I am dropped off at my hotel, I quickly run into the bathroom to jump in the shower and clean off the salt since my dinner reservation is in half an hour. I turn on the water and undress and am immediately halted in my tracks as I suddenly become acutely aware of my reflection in the mirror. The hot water causes the glass to fog and my breasts are slowly engulfed by the steam. In less than two weeks my left chest will be flat, I think. It is a wall I will readily have to face. This is a memory I know I will never forget.

Different but the Same

I like to write my journals in pen the old-fashioned way, but my pink breast cancer EnerGel Liquid Gel Ink pen just ran out.

I adapt quickly by picking up another pen.

Maybe it's different, but life is still the same.

I Don't Want to Die

On my flight home, I miss Aruba already. The carelessness of it. The false sense of reality. Soon, I'll have to face my pending surgery. I'm left with this emptiness of knowing I'll have two and a half months of recovery alone, punctuated by moments of pure pain. I wonder, what do I do now as I wait? And what will come next?

I'm looking out the window at the clouds below when the plane slows down. Then, the pilot guns the engine to go *fast!* The wings shake as we fall in altitude and my stomach drops. I'm scared as the turbulent plane bounces about in the sky. I imagine, in my vivid mind, a nose down decent into the ocean below. And, in my mind of course, we don't have rafts on board.

I begin repeating the mantra: I don't want to die, I don't want to die, I don't want to die, I don't want to die.

When I was first diagnosed with breast cancer, I thought I would die on the operating table. Everyone told me I'd be fine. Now, I just want to live. I want to live a *long,* healthy life.

Learning to Deal

I've been thinking about my bathing suits this week since I've been in the Caribbean Sea. I mostly wear halter tops because they flatter my body type. I had thought I'd be able to salvage at least one post-surgery, but now I'm not so sure. My primary tumor lies on the inner side of my breast and beyond the fabric of the suit. When it is removed, that area will show, and therein lies the problem.

My doctor said there are two types of suture lines: one horizontal and one circular, circulating the alveoli. She thinks they should do the circular version for me. But how wide does this mean? I'm putting my faith in her to choose during the surgery. Whatever the result, I will learn to live with it.

Proposed Surgery Steps

I feel like puking when I review the steps that will occur during my next surgery.

Pre-Step 1: Stop using meds that interfere with surgery

Pre-Step 2: No eating after twelve a.m.

Step 1: Change into hospital gown, clothing and all jewelry off

Step 2: Get injection of blue dye to light up sentinel node

Step 3: Placed in waiting room—*shouldn't there be waiters here serving shots to ease the stress?*

Step 4: Get rolled into hospital operating room

Step 5: Listen to anesthesiologist speak to me

Step 6: Exchange hellos with doctor as she tells me what she'll do

Step 7: Count down from ten

Step 8: Ten, nine, eight . . .

Step 9: Wake up one second later in recovery

Step 10: Hear everyone yell "Hurray!"

I'm still scared after learning the process and now I really feel like puking.

Cards: A Good–Bad Pain

I'm home tonight. There's too much drama elsewhere, and instead I choose to open my get well cards. These are the special ones, the ones I've been saving from special people. I open a card; it makes me cry. I open another card, and I cry even more.

Cards are wonderful things. They are beautiful and have heartfelt words and each sender has added a personal memento, which I reflect upon. They touch my heart and tug at the strings. As a result, they bring pain, but it's a good kind of pain. But, nonetheless, it's pain. Still, I treasure each and every one. I display them and save them and I definitely still want them.

They're good stuff—it just hurts sometimes in a good–bad way.

Circling Minds

There's someone dear to my heart with whom I speak frequently. I feel an urge to speak to her today to get support, not even realizing how scared I feel inside. She can't speak for long, and in desperation, I pick up the phone and call another friend. I struggle to explain how I lost my best friend as a child after her father died and now an adult friend of mine is pulling away after her father died. Death seems to be on my mind as I also recall the recent passing of a very close friend due to a fatal car crash.

My mind is circling. I ruminate about all these things and about why some friends don't return my phone calls. Fear of death, death, fear of loss, loss, all tumble around in my mind in response to my upcoming surgery, which is two days away.

F.E.A.R. I know fear is not rational and remind myself of the acronym: False Events Appearing Real. A pastor once taught me that, and he has been praying for me. He told me he strongly believes God wants me to know I don't need to worry. *I don't need to worry.* I try telling that to my frazzled mind.

The Strange Way We See

Mom calls me today. "Do you want to go out to dinner tomorrow night?" Today is Sunday. On Monday, I will pick her up at the airport at three thirty p.m. Monday is the day before my surgery.

But tomorrow couldn't be the day before the surgery. That was too soon. For so long it was so far away, and now it is right there before me. It didn't make any sense. Tomorrow morning and tomorrow night are not the same day. My brain didn't want to comprehend. Neither did I.

5 A.M.

It's the night before surgery, and all in the house not a creature is stirring, not even a . . . oops, wrong story, but it is the night before my surgery. I am going to bed early and getting up at five thirty a.m. to take a shower since I won't be able to for a few days. I've received several phone calls and texts today wishing me well, which has made me feel loved. My mom is here too, which is a blessing beyond words. I need to sleep to be strong in the morning, and I've been working long hours and getting my house ready for what is to come.

Somehow, I'm much more calm than expected and believe I will be able to sleep. It feels like it's five a.m. already, though. It's so quiet, eerily so, like that stillness just before dawn when the birds start chirping and no else one is up. Maybe the eeriness is just because I know what comes next, and yet I don't, all at the same time.

As strong as I've been, it still hurts to think I'm diseased, which is what I think. Maybe I did something wrong to bring this upon myself?

I'd like to go outside and just breathe. Walk away and just live like this never happened to me. It would be so much easier if it was someone else going into surgery tomorrow. Someone else facing six weeks of recovery. Someone else . . .

Someone else repeats in my mind. Many people's pivotal event in their life is getting married mine, thus far, will be giving my breast away. Somehow it doesn't seem fair.

I say goodnight to my mother, kiss her on the cheek, and lie down, resting my right cheek on the pillow. It's my pillow. The same pillow I've used for quite a long time. The same sheets. The same room. The same apartment. Everything will be the same tomorrow, and yet completely different.

Day of Surgery—Mastectomy #1

5:42 a.m.: I want to jump off a bridge.

6:02 a.m.: I have no choice but to do this.

7:00 a.m.: We are in the hallway outside my surgeon's office. No one is here. My mom and I are standing outside the breast cancer office, and nobody's here. Did I get the date wrong? The time?

7:06 a.m.: An emergency page is made to my general surgeon. *She's on her way.*

7:11 a.m.: The nuclear medicine specialist arrives, and yes, he too had seven a.m. as the time. He says he'll give her fifteen minutes because he has other things he has to attend to.

7:25 a.m.: Just as he is about to leave, she arrives.

7:30 a.m.: I get the injection and am told to massage the breast for half an hour.

7:40 a.m.: My general surgeon comes in and marks my breast.

7:45 a.m.: I am walked over to the hospital.

7:53 a.m.: Information is taken from me.

8:00 a.m.: More information is taken from me.

8:13 a.m.: My anesthesiologist comes to speak with me. He understands that I'm nervous as this is my first surgery ever, other than my wisdom teeth. He tells me he will give me an injection as soon as we're in the operating room to calm me down.

8:15 a.m.: I go to the restroom to remove my tampon and realize my hair is a mess.

8:19 a.m.: My plastic surgeon arrives to look at my breast and marks her incisions with a sharpie based upon my general surgeon's earlier drawings.

8:22 a.m.: I am rolled away. I can't help thinking I'm not ready. Everything went so fast; my hair's not even put up. There are a million hands on me immediately after I'm rolled into the operating room. I'm sitting upright in as close to a fetal position as I can get, and I'm shaking.

Everyone's getting ready and they inform me a student will be observing. I am asked to move onto the operating table, lie down, and put my head in a support. They strap down my legs and the anesthesiologist comes in. He looks different in his scrub cap. He puts my port in, but the first one doesn't thread well so he has to try again.

That's it. I don't remember anything else.

I wake up in the recovery room, and I'm told they don't have a bed for me yet. My mom and Daniel, who drove in from NYC, come in to say hello. I thank them profusely for being there. They spend the rest of the day with me as I drift in and out of sleep. We talk. I say, I'm sleepy. They say to take a nap. My nurse comes in and is fantastic. She is attentive. She checks on me and brings me things I need; she has great bedside manners. Evening comes and my mom finally goes home to get some sleep. I ask Daniel to stay longer, and he does.

In the morning, the nurse makes me walk to the bathroom for a sponge bath. Pretty soon it's time to go, and they sit me in a wheel chair. I have a pillow on my lap and the pink, leopard blanket my friends gave me is wrapped around my body. I am wheeled out of the hospital when my mom pulls up, and I gingerly maneuver from the wheelchair into the car *with much help* and we go home.

Finality

It's over.

I made it through the surgery.

The cancer is gone.

Hallelujah!

Chapter 3 Tips

Letting go—clearing away the clutter

While going through cancer, the patient cannot control much. So, sometimes it helps to focus on something that can be controlled and to create a pleasant, soothing environment when everything else seems to be a complete mess.

With that said, you still need to deal with what you can't control, which means you need to let go. Letting go is twofold. First, you need to let go of the mind. This can be accomplished through journaling or mind mapping, with an old-fashioned pen and paper or on a computer, or by doing a guided meditation if you can't think of anything to write or mind map about. Second, you need to physically remove surrounding clutter in order to create a sacred space, which can be a small area of a room, an entire room, or, for the really ambitious, a whole house.

Journaling: I simply pick up a pen and paper or an electronic device and write whatever is in and on my mind. When first starting out, you can set a timer for one minute and then write down everything you're thinking about, fearful of, happy about, dreading, or excited for. I have learned there are no wrong answers.

As you continue to do this every day, you can slowly increase the amount of writing time until you no longer need the timer. Julia Cameron calls these her "morning pages." In her book *The Artist's Way*, she suggests writing three pages every day without censoring anything and without re-reading them:

There is no wrong way to do morning pages ... Pages are meant to be, simply, the act of moving the hand across the page and writing down whatever comes to mind. Nothing is too petty, too silly, too stupid, or too weird to be included ... (they) are the primary tool of creative recovery.

Mind Mapping: In mind mapping, you simply write down an idea in the center of a page and then branch out in every direction from the central idea writing down everything that relates to the main idea. This creates a visual map of what's on your mind.

Guided Meditations: I found these through searching for meditation apps on my phone or tablet or searching for guided meditations in iTunes, on the internet, or YouTube. They also can be checked out from the library.

Clearing the Clutter: In my home, everything has its own home, where it belongs, and I try to return it when I am not using it. Keys belong in one place, sunglasses another, shirts, pants, etc. If things don't have a home, they end up pilling up. Emilee Barnes talks about the importance of having a specific place. Each item is either important enough to have a specific place to reside or it's well suited to be discarded. Getting in the habit of putting everything in its place and actually discarding things is, of course, easier said than done. It is easy to make attachments to things and difficult to let them go. So I remind myself this is hard stuff and to be patient.

I have learned a few decluttering tips over the years, and I do my best to follow them.

- This tip comes from Emilee Barnes's *101 Ways to Clear Out the Clutter*. Decluttering is focusing on what is no longer needed, so walk around saying, "I don't need you," and identify what can be given away to someone else.

- Mary Lambert discusses sorting in *Clearing the Clutter: For Good Feng Shui*. Spend five to ten minutes each day making quick sorting decisions. I try to be honest—items not used in years are just taking up valuable space. And if I keep thinking I should give an item away, that's a sign to take the bold step and move forward by actually giving it away; someone else is waiting to enjoy my clutter. When sorting, sort items into five piles: junk, thrift store/friends, things needing repair, things in the wrong room, and transitional items. "Things needing repair" should be repaired promptly or repositioned in the "junk" pile. "Transitional items" are not seasonal but rather items you *can't let go of yet* so you'll check back in six months.
- When purchasing something new, picture in your mind what item you can get rid of that will be replaced by this new item, and as soon as you get home, exchange the items.
- Items that go in and out every day, such as purses and keys, need accessible homes. Bins, drawers, and shelves can be labeled and then are ideal for organizing these keepables.

Cleaning: Cleaning is necessary, but this is the time in life to focus more on "what must get done" tasks rather than making the home immaculate. I also found some cleaning agencies provide free cleaning services for cancer patients (see the resources list).

Overall, I write down goals every day. They can be little goals or big goals as I aim to accomplish a little every day. I start each day with the worst, or hardest, thing on the list first. Then, I often find it wasn't as bad as I expected, and now since it's done, the rest will be easier.

Questions to ask the general surgeon prior to the surgery

-How long will I be in the hospital?

-Can you explain the recovery process and how long recovery takes? How much help will I need at home after surgery? Will driving be restricted? For how long?

-How long will the pain last? Can I pick up pain pills in advance? Will they affect my digestive track and cause constipation or diarrhea? What about anxiety the night before or the day of surgery? And what do I do about medications I normally take the day of the surgery and when I'm in the hospital?

-How many drains am I likely to have? Do you provide drainage camisoles or shirts to hold the drains? How do I care for the drains?

-In taking out the sentinel lymph nodes, how many other lymph nodes will be removed and how will this affect my body? Will it cause lymphedema (swelling due to removed lymph nodes) and affect my activities like flying or scuba diving?

-What will the surgery pathology report show?

-If my tumor is ER+ (estrogen receptive positive), PR+ (progesterone responsive growth) and/or BRCA+ (breast cancer gene mutation), will you recommend I have an oophorectomy? Or a total hysterectomy? How quickly would I need that surgery?

-How will you be certain you have clean margins (no cancer cells in the outer edge of the tissue sampled)?

Questions to ask the plastic surgeon prior to the surgery

-How many reconstruction surgeries have you done? Can I see images of your work? Can I speak to other patients?

-Are you in my network? What will my expenses be if you're not?

-What are my reconstructive options?

-What will my follow-up schedule be like with you after surgery?

Questions to ask the plastic surgeon if you choose implants

-What type of implants do you offer? What is the difference between them?

-How long do implants last? How will time affect the implant? What is the process for replacement?

-What happens if I gain or lose weight?

-Can you see behind implants to diagnose future cancers? What methods assess areas with implants?

-What are issues people have had with implants?

-How do I verbalize to others I have implants because of cancer?

How to pick a nutritionist

-Are they knowledgeable about nutrition, especially nutrition relating to cancer?

-Have they been practicing for a long time with reputable credentials?

-Do they have a long record of success?

-Will I be able to follow the new guidelines? Are they doable?

-Do I have special and specific nutritional needs that they can address?

-Will they put my goals first and tailor the meetings to that end?

-Am I required to purchase supplements from the nutritionist?

-Do I feel confident and comfortable with them and their experience, knowledge, and skills?

-Do I like them and feel we can work together?

-Will they give me recipes and/or meal guides to follow?

-Are they close to where I live so transportation won't be a problem?

After all of this, close your eyes and listen to your intuition. If no answer arises, keep searching.

Things families, friends, and caregivers can do

-Offer to listen and call the patient just to say "hi." Some days they may want to talk, and others they may not, but it's nice to have friends and people show they care. And if they tell you they don't want to talk or don't want advice, don't take it personally. This behavior just means they need to process some things themselves, but they may still want you to listen to them and be a sounding board.

-Offer to drive them to an appointment and wait in the waiting room with them.

-Offer to help them clear out some clutter in the kitchen and go explore a health food store together.

-Make smoothies together.

-Go for a walk with them.

-Bring them a magazine, or better yet, a journal to write in with a special pen or pencil. This doesn't have to be something expensive. Any pen or pencil can be made special by wrapping yarn or ribbon around it. Beads can be added to the yarn for special effect or you can wrap a feather on the pencil instead.

-With kids, make a journal. Take several sheets of regular copy paper, hold them together, and fold them in half. Punch two holes along the folded side—which will become the spine. Thread string through the holes and tie them together once threaded. Decorate the cover together with crayons, colored pencils, or markers. Kids can also make a special pen or pencil!

-Pre-surgery: Make a hospital basket with essentials for them to bring to the surgery: tissues, a special blanket, socks, mints/gum, an adult coloring book, dark chocolate, snacks, juice boxes.

-Post-surgery: Help them order a "compression sleeve" to help prevent lymphedema when lifting heavy objects or going on a plane since lymph nodes will be removed. In order to buy one, you will need to take their arm measurements and then they can be picked up at a medical supply store or ordered online. They come in skin colors or in a bright array of patterns.

Late November - December

Chapter 4—So, This Is Cancer Free?

After my first mastectomy, life was different, mainly physically. I had never had a surgery before, other than having my wisdom teeth pulled out, so I had no concept of what pain was or could be and how it truly felt. Showering wasn't allowed so I took baths in six inches of water, and I learned the hard way my doctor's prescribed six weeks of recovery actually meant six weeks. Overall, I found healing is a step-by-step process and the idea of one step forward, one step back is truly based on real world experience.

The Truth Hurts

My general surgeon comes into the hospital room early in the morning and sits down. "We found a tumor in one of your lymph nodes, your sentinel lymph node."

So, what does this mean? The cancer cells have spread out of the breast into the start of the lymphatic system. *And my main fear*: chemotherapy may be necessary, meaning I will lose my hair.

Three Types of Pain

I've discovered there are three types of pain:

Zingers—pain that shoots right through you.

Dull Aching Pain—pain that is continuously present and persistent.

Non-Dull Aching Pain—pain at a level between the two, which is not shooting, but is a larger, more intense pain that radiates through the breast. It does not last too long.

Post-Surgery Headaches

I've been having horrific headaches ever since the surgery. The pain medication helps to reduce them, a little.

My general surgeon, wonderful person that she is, calls me to ask how I'm doing. I tell her about the headaches and she informs me they are possibly a side effect of the surgery. Amazingly, after I speak to her, they go away. But, shhh, don't tell anybody or they may come back!

The First Time Ever I Saw Your Face

My general surgeon unveils my breast in front of my mom and me. It doesn't hurt much when she unwraps the bandages. Because I'm looking down at it, I can't really see much, though I can tell it isn't completely flat: there's a little bump since my plastic surgeon filled up the expander somewhat during the surgery. It looks like a horizontal line of tape covering stitches, running across what used to be my breast. The stitches for the lymph nodes are below the skin and can only be felt, not seen. My mom's response: it's a very long scar reaching far across my breast, not the expected circle.

The Tetherball Game

Today is my first post-surgery doctor's visit with my plastic surgeon. I am very nervous and fearful that whatever she will do will hurt. My chest is very tight and I'm imaging pulling, and pushing, and poking, and prodding, despite the fact I'm not a cow.

When I arrive, my PA checks my drainage and likes what she sees. My drain recordings show a good reduction in the amount of fluid draining since surgery into the round suction bubbles hanging out of my body. She says my doctor will most likely take one drain out. Both drain measurements are low, so I ask about taking both out.

"Oh, we never take both drains out at the same time," she responds. I'm bummed as I feel like I've been tethered. In having them, I've grown a new respect for people with bladder bags.

My doctor comes and says taking the sutures out will pinch. It doesn't, but the strangest feeling is when she pulls out the drain tube. It's the diameter of a straw but is a harder plastic. I can feel it move inside me, through my chest, like a snake slithering and being sucked out until it reaches the surface of my skin and pops completely out of my body. I know of nothing to compare it to—it's nothing I've ever experienced before. I feel relief.

Then comes the gauze. My doctor explains that she can get about 10 mL more liquid out through pushing and rubbing across my removed breast area, so she proceeds to do so. Finally, she tapes me up with more gauze and gives me instructions to continue to change the gauze and measure the remaining liquid accumulating in the remaining drain. I am to call in three days to report in and see about removing the second drain.

I am excited for the thought of being tetherball free!

Every Breath

I'm sitting in my rocking recliner. I can hear the fish tank gurgling, the distant sound of the shower, and some cars passing by. While the TV is before me, it is off. I need a moment of respite—a moment to myself to relax. It's hard to relax, though, when as soon as I do, I immediately feel my "breast," or what is left of it. My "breast" is aware of my every breath.

Unburying Roots

It's hard to understand something unless you've gone through it yourself. People with breast cancer share the "bond," if you will, of similar pain.

Before my surgery, I couldn't comprehend what pain meant. Was it like a splinter in your finger? A cramp in your leg but located in your breast? Now, I feel pain in areas I never imagined were related. My lower back aches since I am always standing—it's more comfortable to be vertical and sometimes sitting just doesn't do it. My left upper arm is numb due to severed nerve endings from lymph node removal. This feels like a rubber band is wound tightly around my upper arm in a continuous blood pressure cuff. Doing a fly motion feels like I'm lifting a weight that is too heavy, when in actuality I have nothing in my hand. My sternum hurts too. The worst is leaning forward, which causes my pectoral muscles to tweak, shooting agonizing pain through my "breast"—even simply resting my arm against my body puts tension on the breast area.

I'm doing breathing exercises to prevent pneumonia and arm exercises to work on my range of motion. The arm exercises consist of walking my fingers up the wall and thus raising my arm, with the goal of reaching my arm straight up, similar to a child asking a question in school. This simple motion is painful. I sing the yodeling song of the mountain climber on *The Price Is Right* to divert my focus. But still, it sends pain from my armpit to the inner side of my chest. Clothing doesn't help. Soft shirts, which I never considered before, feel rough and my camisole strap is too tight even though it's extra loose and thin. I guess I understand now what pain is like.

The New Worst

The worst is propelling my breast out of bed. *And* the "rubber band" tightening around my upper arm. *And* the pain I feel every time I lean forward.

A New Lease on Life

I'm having family over for Thanksgiving. We're going out for dinner, but I still can't shower and do my hair well, so I make an appointment at a local salon. Since I rarely get my hair cut, and lately my classmate has been doing it near school since she's also a hairstylist, I don't have a personal stylist in my town. I do know of a local place inside an old church and they say they can fit me in.

When I meet my hairstylist, we consult about what I want done and I tell her I'm in pain so to please use extra care. I can see sympathy take over her, and I blurt out the reason. This, however, results in shock crossing her face that someone so young had to have a mastectomy. She walks me over to the sinks, and I have to explain everything all over to the girl who is washing my hair because I'm afraid leaning back will cause tremendous pain. Another look of shock from another person I've never spoken to before. I sit down, take a deep breath, and grimace as she helps lean me back to position me for the washing.

The warm water feels nice as she runs the showerhead along the top of my head and neck and then massages the shampoo in. I'm OK as long as I stay still, and I'm already feeling so much cleaner so I'm glad I came. Since the surgery, I've been using dry shampoo because I can't lift my left arm up to shampoo and condition in the bath. As a result, my hair is completely disgusting at this point. She doesn't comment on it.

My hair has grown very long and has a slight red tint to its dark brown color so once I'm back in the stylist's chair, she asks if I want to cut it.

"Just a trim please," I say. "I really just needed it washed and blown out." She tenderly blows it straight and dry, and when it's done, I feel ready to face my family and go out to eat for the first time since surgery.

Thanksgiving Blessings

Today is Thanksgiving. A wonderful day all around. I've been texting all my friends and enjoying all their responses—even the ones who've "forgotten" me, no longer recognizing my phone number. My mom has been making great food for me at home while she's been visiting, but sometimes I've felt I've been trapped here for years. What must astronauts do? Serious meditation?

We dress up, carefully for me, head out, and have a traditional feast, great conversation, and yes, I even choose to say grace! Plus, when we return home, I have a nice private petting session with my furry cat ball.

Now, I'm having a pajama night with my mom—satisfaction guaranteed! I feel completely full, in fact a little overdosed. Peace. Gratitude. Silence. Amen.

Meditation

Today, I start meditating again. It's not that I wasn't before, it's just that today was different. I needed it more somehow. I've needed it for a long time, but I stopped myself. There's something so pure about meditating, so relieving and reviving, but sometimes I don't want to go there. I want to be out of balance, out of control, living on the wayside of the edge. Now, I need the balance. Truly, I always have, but . . . here enters the "but" again.

There are no excuses. It's the same as going to the gym for me. I don't want to go, but when I'm dressed and standing up, I'm ready to go out the door. Yes, some days I get there and don't think I'll make it more than two minutes on the elliptical, but usually two becomes four, and maybe I don't make it half an hour, but I've done something. Then, I breathe in white light and exhale black smoke. After working out, I'm so much better: I'm sweaty and drained and so wonderfully *alive*.

Yoga is the same. Fill me with divine, white light and let the demons out. My abdomen, diaphragm, and lungs fill with clear, pure air, and then release the negative toxins, which have gone stale as I've held them within. I'm surrounded with a cone of white light. I'm safe and alone in my thoughts, and the pain releases in tears. All the pain I've been holding onto for years, and especially the stress of the last six months releases: pitch black tar that's been eating up my insides is now ready to go. I'm ready to release and move on.

My First Shower

I finally get in the shower today. My mom is right outside in case I need help. I'm afraid the water will hit my breast, so I've been taking baths. Also, I've been petrified I would drop the soap and have to bend over to pick it up in the falling stream of water.

My mom suggests trying to take a shower but waiting to wash my hair until I'm more comfortable, so I take her advice. Borrowing her shower cap, I dress myself up like a cafeteria lady, ground myself with courage, and step into the shower.

The water feels nice as it flows down my body. It's hot, but not too hot, and I manage to avoid my breast since I'm not ready to attempt that yet. I gingerly use my left hand to clean part of my body as best as possible. This is hard because I still can't lift my left arm very well and have the continual rubber band-like pressure around it since the mastectomy was on my left side. But I know I need to start using it more.

It's a comfort to know my mom is here and it's scary to think she will only be here for four more days.

Searching for the Light

Behind the closed doors of a woman's heart,

a young child lies crying.

Maybe she lost her toy,

maybe she lost her mom,

maybe something's just not right.

I don't want to be a lost toy,

or a lost mom,

or a young girl crying in the dark.

Let me see a way out of this

and into the white healing light.

Imaginary Hurt

I still don't understand the concept that anything happening to my breast won't hurt. It's still there, sort of. Maybe, it's not, and I'm still in denial. The truth is: it won't hurt because it is numb, but that doesn't mean my brain has registered that fact. My brain is scared and my heart is afraid. Is there really a difference?

Today, I find out if I need chemo or not. This will affect my entire body. This will "hurt." This is not something I will quickly recover from.

The Reality as the Saga Continues

Today I go with my mom to see both doctors for my post-operation appointments. I'm bracing myself because I'm expecting to hear the bad news: you need chemotherapy. Despite this fear, I keep hugging my general surgeon. I guess even though she's butchered my chest open, I really like her. And she has removed the bad, black mass from inside me.

First, we meet with my plastic surgeon and inadvertently she spills the beans that I need another surgery.

Another surgery? How can I need another surgery? Is this common? I didn't even know this was a possibility; I never imagined this. I thought once they took off the breast, everything would be done except for reconstruction.

When I walked into the office, I thought the cancer was already gone and now I'm facing a basketball court wall graffitied with "Ha, ha I'm still here." Suddenly, I'm once again in a game I never wanted to play, and it keeps coming back to haunt me.

Both of my doctors tell me I'm healing really well, but the pathology shows we "need to take more tissue." The reports show a clip, which was put in during one of the biopsies, went missing. They're not sure if it fell out or if it is still inside me. So, the first step will be to have another mammogram to see if the clip lights up. If it does, it means one of the areas diagnosed with cancer is still inside me. Also, my general surgeon feels the margin around one tumor wasn't large enough and they found several small DCIS tumors they were not even aware of.

More tumors. *More tumors!* I'm dumbstruck. How am I ever going to get well if they keep finding *more tumors* and need to do *more surgeries?* My question as to whether I will need chemo will not be answered today so that still looms in the future. I don't know what to hold on to. I don't know what the future holds. Will I ever get back to a normal life? All I can hold on to is knowing that I need to put one foot in front of the other and wait for the future to unfold.

The Truth About Separation

I hear a plane overhead. My mom is gone. There is nothing really to say about separation except it hurts. It leaves me feeling alone, and I don't know what to do with myself until I find a task that refocuses me, redirecting my mind by grabbing my attention away from the painful moment of separation. Truth doesn't lie; instead, it stares me right in the face and says, "This person is gone now so deal with it." Either step up to the plate or wither in self-loathing. When I recognize this is happening, I remind myself to take the first few moments to feel. I internalize the loss and then pick myself up, turn around, and courageously grab some inner strength. Sometimes, there is no other choice.

Dressing 101

You put your right foot in, you put your right foot out. You put your right foot in and you shake it all about . . . I've found it's easiest to put my socks on while sitting on the floor. Undies and pants require leaning against my arm chair and balancing on one leg while the second leg maneuvers through the hole. Tops are even tougher since I have to move my arm, lifting it straight up or to the side. I'm sure it varies from patient to patient but I've found getting my left arm (the side of my mastectomy) in first is a clear necessity with careful sliding of the clothing article up my arm and into place. This must be followed by gingerly moving my right arm in through the opposite hole. I haven't worn a bra yet, and I don't plan to for a *long time,* but even camisoles cause problems. Multiple times I have screamed while getting stuck putting a camisole on over my head. Today, I have definitively determined it is best to use a large one that I can slide up my body from the floor and then slip my arms through the straps as it passes my hands. I have found loose button-down shirts or those with a zipper are the easiest. No matter how soft the material is and feels, inevitably, it will still feel rough against my raw skin.

Creativity

I have an itch on my back.

I use a hair brush to reach it, and I'm satisfied.

Stretching to Excess

I recall times when I've wanted something so badly I would've done anything to get it. This is one of those times. I want to heal so much, I want to be better, I want to be able to drive. I need to get to the laundromat, the supermarket, the bank, a meditation class, the bagel shop, my favorite Indian restaurant: these are now my current desires, and I'm trying hard to get there. I was getting better, feeling stronger, and doing my exercises three times a day. Since I had almost reached full extension of my arm, which means driving privileges, I decided to increase my stretches and do them whenever I think of them: maybe eight, or even ten times a day. It takes only a day or two before I feel agonizing pain. My expander feels as heavy as an overfull water balloon pulling down on my breast from the inside.

The actual intensity of the pain is that multiplied by one hundred! I want it out, *just rip it out, please!*

So, I call my PA at the plastic surgeon's office. She tells me it is just like with any exercise in that I had, "gone too far." She instructs me to completely stop doing my exercises for a few days. *Stop?*

So, I wait. And I agonize. And I wait some more as the pain slowly subsides.

The Missing Clip

Today, I am at the breast center for my post-mastectomy mammogram, mainly to see if I still have the "missing clip" inside me. It's kind of like a mystery. Will it or won't it be there? I can't believe I have to do this, but I'm in good spirits.

After putting on my white spa gown, a.k.a. robe, they lead me into a room. The technician has me remove the left side of my gown, causing that side to fall down beside me suspended by the belt, and the rest to hang diagonally across my back. She positions me around the machine and clamps down on what was once my breast and now is skin over my expander, a round red piece of plastic or something like that, filled somewhat with liquid.

Pinch, squeeze, hold breath, release. Reposition and repeat several times.

When we're all done, she lets me see the images, though she's probably not supposed to. And there it is, glaring bright on the dark image: my missing clip. Shit. I'm immediately depressed. There is the proof I will need another surgery. I still have cancer *inside me.*

Nightmares and Sleeping Techniques

I wake in a pool of sweat gasping for breath.

After my heartbeat calms down, I go to the bathroom. When I return, I do a whole body relaxation in an attempt to relax enough so I can fall back asleep and have calm dreams.

Cue the nightmare

In the mammogram room I stand before the monstrous machine. My robe hangs lifeless below my waist. The tech places my breast between the plates and slowly tightens down, squeezing my breast, until it's as flat as a pancake. She squeezes it more and more, tighter and *tighter*. She steps behind the counter as the plates reach their maximum point. Pain, pain, *pain!* A blood-curdling scream. The machine releases.

Falling to the floor, tears flood out of my eyes while I hold my chest, supporting what must be a tumor the size of Uranus.

Stage directions: Black and white lights flash.

Calmly the announcer says: Well we'll have to do the rest of the test by sonogram; there'll be no more screaming allowed.

Stage directions: End scene.

Chapter 4 Tips

Whole body relaxation

Sleep often eludes me since becoming a cancer sufferer. However, I have found some techniques to help: listening to a guided meditation or doing a whole body relaxation.

In this whole body relaxation, I lie flat on my back and progressively tense and release every body part, starting at the feet and traveling up to the head. As I progress through each body part, I make sure to really focus my mind on that specific body part. Often I find myself getting sleepy before I have even finished. If I am not asleep or sleepy, I am at least much more relaxed by the end of the sequence.

The steps

Step 1. Lie on back.

Step 2: Imagine tensing each body part in the order below, holding the tense for a count of ten, and moving to the next one.

- Toes
- Top of your feet
- Bottom of your feet
- Heels of your feet
- Ankles
- Calves
- Shins
- Knees
- Thighs

- Hamstrings
- Glutes
- Pelvis
- Stomach
- Lower back
- Upper back

Step 3. Tense and relax your upper back. Here, focus on expanding the ribcage out to the side with each breath and then relaxing inward with each exhale. Take four breaths here with a count of ten as well.

Step 4. Focus on your chest. Inhale with one long breath through the nose while counting to ten. Exhale through your mouth for the same count of ten. Repeat this four times.

Step 5. Tense each body part below for a count of ten, release and relax it, then move to the next one.

- Biceps
- Triceps
- Elbows
- Lower arms
- Each individual finger—your thumbs, your pointer fingers, your middle fingers, your ring fingers, and then your pinky fingers
- Neck
- Face
- Brain

Step 6. Imagine squeezing your brain for ten and then release.

For a *deeper relaxation,* you can separate the body into sides by relaxing the right side and then the left as you travel up the body. Or you can make a loop coming up the right side and then traveling down the left.

For a *quicker sequence*, perhaps you're in a doctor's office waiting for an appointment and don't have time for the whole body, you can group muscles together as below.

Quicker relaxation

Follow this order:

- Feet
- Lower legs
- Upper legs
- Glutes
- Pelvis
- Stomach
- Lower back
- Upper back
- Chest
- Upper arms
- Lower arms
- Hands
- Neck
- Face
- Brain

While tensing your face, play with this and stick out your tongue as far as you can to make a lion face. When I taught yoga to children, we would do this whole body relaxation and the kids especially loved making lion faces. If you try and look in the mirror, it looks pretty funny!

Questions to ask the general surgeon after the surgery

-What is the final stage and grade of my tumor? Was it aggressive, moderate, or slow?

-Were the margins clean? How large were they? If they are not large enough, when is the next surgery to get clean margins?

-What were the results of the lymph node biopsy? Were lymph nodes involved? How many were involved? Were they infected with the same type of cancer cells?

-What is the hormone receptor status? Is the cancer ER / PR positive or negative? Or a mixture? Can you explain what this means and how it affects the treatment plan? Is the cancer her2-positive? Can you explain this and how it affects the treatment plan?

-Was the cancer tested for an "oncotype" and what does that mean? How do these results affect the treatment plan?

-How often do you see this particular type of cancer, and what is the usual outcome and recurrence rate?

-What can I do now and in the months and years ahead to ensure I remain cancer free?

Things families, friends, and caregivers can do

-Send a card or bring one with dinner, checking first to make sure company is welcome. (Many cards can be found with appropriate sentiments if you are at a loss for words or not sure if your words are the right ones to say.)

-Watch TV together or bring over a movie.

-Take a walk together.

February

Winning the Breast Cancer Battle

Chapter 5—Surgery #2, If It's Still Broke, Fix It

With breast cancer, I've come to learn that road A might start out as A but may then morph into something else like: *B, no, C, no . . . G!* My "first" mastectomy wasn't the end I had expected. After having a missing clip and not wide enough margins, I now had to wait in peaked anticipation for my next surgery. My moods became much like a rollercoaster, wavering above and below the threshold of happiness.

Dreaming of Another Surgery

I woke from a dream this morning. I was in the surgery waiting room again, but this time for my second surgery. I was dressed in my gown with my nonslip socks. It was very quiet. My eyes were darting around and I couldn't sit still so I went to relieve my bladder. Returning to my room, I was told someone had been looking for me. They told me the hospital decided to do a special service today and all the parking was free.

At some point all the lights went out, and it was pitch black in the room since there weren't any windows. I did not freak out. My anesthesiologist came over to "check in," but it wasn't the doctor I like, so I had to fight even harder to not freak out.

I wondered if I would hug my knees like I did during the first surgery when they rolled me away. I wondered if they would wrap my body in a warm blanket—I was cold so I needed it. I wondered if they would overstretch my arm and destroy all the work I had been doing over the past two months. I wondered.

Sinking Ships

Today has been a rough day. I went to get blood work done, and after listening to a song in the waiting area, I cried through the rest of the appointment. I tell the phlebotomist I'm scared since this is my first blood draw since the surgery, and I cry yet again. A second phlebotomist speaks to me and tells me about his wife who had kidney cancer and explains what saved her was a transplant. He tells me right now I need to make myself number one. He says, "attitude is everything." I have heard this before from Rose in the hair salon, and other people, but sometimes I can't muster the strength.

I stop at the post office on the way home to mail holiday cards, which makes me cry even more and lasts for the duration of the ride home. My landlord is at the door, and in seeing me crying, she says, "I told you I would drive you."

"It's not that. I'm just sad," I mumble in reply.

Sometimes, or maybe a lot of times, life doesn't go the way it's planned. Dreams have to be pushed off into the distance. One day has to be pushed back to another when maybe I will be able to let in the sunshine to lift my mood and attitude back to where it belongs. And though I wanted to drive myself, I have to admit: I wasn't quite ready.

In the Midst of Darkness, I Realize There Is Light

After having overstretched and healed, my PA told me today to start stretching again, *slowly*, so my arm doesn't get stiff. I do and to my surprise, I do well. My inner elbow doesn't have the strain and pull I was expecting, and I am able to walk my fingers way up the wall. This is progress, but for some reason today I am sad, which can't be explained. Maybe it's because the sun is shining and it seems like such a normal day for everyone else but not for me? I've been hit with the pity bug, thinking other cancer patients have it much worse than me, yet my pain is real too. Maybe the point is not to lessen my struggles, but to realize others may also be suffering or even suffering more. Albert Camus said, "In the midst of winter—I suddenly found that there was in me an invincible summer," and I feel this way. I know within me I have a light that will shine out of this darkness and shine brightly enough to lead others on.

Bearing the Pain

My cat jumps on me. She just wants to snuggle on my lap, but somehow my skin gets tight, and I feel it in my breast. I stiffen, and then try to settle so she can settle and lie there as I stroke her fur. We both relinquish love and affection towards one another. Because I find it more important to be loved, I succumb and bear the pain.

A Place Filled with Love

I've been reading another book about breast cancer. Some of it I already know. Some of it makes me cry in thinking about how this is affecting my life. I just sit staring out the window, watching and hearing the wind. The trees just stand there swaying and bending, but not going anywhere. I would like to go someplace far away from here. Someplace sunshiny and tasty, like oranges freshly peeled—where it's not too hot nor too cold and where I can walk right onto the white sandy beach and into the turquoise blue sea. There I'll have no worries, and all this would be a fleeting bad dream. It's a happy spot without disease and where family surrounds me. I would have motivation and courage and love. Love for everybody, but most importantly pink, strengthening love for me.

The first time I recall making a vision board was with Jennifer Louden, and I still have it to this day. She supplied the materials so participants in the workshop could focus on finding images that spoke to us and then create our final image. I decide to make a vision board.

Heightened Awareness and Those Who Are Worse Off

I haven't been writing lately. I guess I've reached a point where life just moves along. Everything stands in peaked anticipation, but not of the good kind. No word on the second surgery date yet, so I can't schedule my primary care doctor's appointment nor my blood work. I've reduced the pain killers but still can't get used to this numbness in my arm, nor the weight in my left breast area. And I've fallen into the burden of the "why me?" scenario over the past few days.

My sister-in-law tries to help by reminding me there are those worse off. I appreciate her effort to help, but when I'm physically suffering, my heart and mind do not have the capacity to feel sympathy for someone else. Yes, some may be worse off but does that knowledge reduce my pain? Right now, all I can focus on is me. In fact, at this exact moment the world revolves solely around me. Tomorrow, I'll think of someone else, but not today.

Just Scream

Aaaagggghhhhhh!

Don't worry; there's nothing wrong.

Well actually, there is. I need to scream. I'm stressed. I found out the surgery is in two weeks. We're stupid, this human race, always trying to better ourselves and resulting in giving ourselves diseases.

Rock Bottom

I want to die. There's no other way to say it. I want to die. I don't want to wake up from the operating room table. Take me and put me out of my misery like a dog. I don't want to get up. I'm not thinking about family and friends who will be left behind; I just don't want to do it anymore. I don't want to be. So, take it away.

Why do I need another surgery? I can't do this again. Months of recovery. Isolation. Pain. Please help me, God, bring me back to you. Let me roam with my father, my grandparents, and uncle. Haven't I suffered enough?

Surgery #2

My second surgery was on Friday, February 14. No Valentine's Day for me. Or maybe my Valentine's Day gift was the gift of life, the gift of self-sustenance. My surgeons told me this would be a quick recovery of four days—over the weekend—but I still had my fears after my lengthy recovery from my *first* mastectomy.

Today, four days later, I'm feeling pretty good and am thinking they were right. All my fears about this second surgery to finish the initial mastectomy were proven false. It reminds me of learning about FAITH at church. The acronym translating into Full Assurance In The Heart. I need to have more faith in my doctors and God.

Unexpected News

My second post-surgery checkup today with my well-respected and trusted general surgeon went like this:

Doc: You look great, Karen. Your range of motion is excellent.

Me: (Big smile) So, what is next? What do I have to do now?

Doc: Well, you'll set up your next appointment with me in six weeks, plus your next MRI of your other breast in March based off your period, and also your next mammogram. And you need to call your oncologist right away.

Me: OK, to talk about the five-year pill?

Doc: Yes.

Me: So . . . I won't need chemo?

Doc: (She shakes her head NO.)

Me: I don't need chemo? *I don't need chemo!*

Chapter 5 Tips

Make a vision board

Supplies: A piece of poster board, foam core board, or cardboard, and several magazines, glue, and scissors.

Artmaking: Cut out images that make you feel happy; ones that make you feel like you're on top of the world with no worries or cares. Arrange them on your poster board. Try to slightly overlap your images and keep them tightly together. If there is time to spare, cut out many images; if this will be a short artmaking session, focus on five images. Glue them down.

Analysis: Ask a partner to help you with the next part. Alternately, you can make a voice memo of yourself if you don't have a partner readily available. Your partner's job is to record everything you say, exactly how you say it, as you answer the following questions. This will allow you to focus on interpreting the vision board and not worry about remembering what you've said. Before you begin, take a moment to have your partner write down the questions.

Hold your vision board and look at it as you answer each of the following questions:

1. What do you want to tell me?

2. What do I need to know right now?

3. What is the most important thing for me to remember from you?

4. How does this vision board make me feel?

5. How can I give myself permission to take this feeling with me?

6. What would I most like to create next?

Questions to ask the general surgeon

-What is the likelihood of metastases?

Things families, friends, and caregivers can do

-Adults and kids: Make a vision board together.

-Bring over an adult coloring book and pencils and do a page together.

-Order a "Fighting Pretty" package or pink boxing gloves.

-Go for a walk together.

March – September

Chapter 6—What Comes Next? Radiation, Chemotherapy, Lymphedema, and Reconstruction

After my single mastectomy surgeries are behind me, I find out one doctor's "no" is another doctor's "yes." Radiation and chemotherapy don't turn out the way I expect. I fight right on through as my journey progresses. New experiences galore cross my path and old experiences become new again, like playing tennis and making new friends. When I am barely a shadow of myself, I encounter reconstruction and dancing along the way. And though none of us want it, I find out "membership" has its privileges.

Radiology?

I meet with the radiologist in the basement floor of the cancer building. I wait to be called in, thinking I'm going to need radiation. To my surprise, the doctor says he doesn't believe I need it. He says he trusts my surgeon and she feels she got wide enough margins so there is no radiation necessary. This is great news! I know other breast cancer sufferers who have needed radiation. They all explained to me how they had to have a cast made with them holding their arm up. The cast is so they will be able to assume the exact position every day and radiation is every day for varying lengths, but often six weeks. It then left their skin very tough and affected their implant so they had to have another surgery to repair the damage. I had already planned to do my radiation at the hospital across the street from where I live so I could do it before going to work, but now I don't need to do it at all! Yippie!

Yesterday and Today

Yesterday, I was talking to Alex. I said, "Maybe I want to have chemo. Maybe it's an experience I need to have." What if humans go through their lives with certain tasks they need to accomplish? Could this be one of mine?

Before I went to bed, I wrote him this message:

I've changed my mind. I don't want chemo. I mean, really, what was I thinking?

To Chemo or Not to Chemo?

My surgeon told me to make an appointment with an oncologist so I scheduled it, but didn't have any fear because she told me I wouldn't need chemotherapy.

I arrive and wait in the waiting area, which is completely decorated with vines of purple flowers hanging from the ceiling and laying on the tables in front of me. Some of the "tables" are old trunks. My name is called, and I am taken to a room where I meet with the medical assistant. Shortly afterward, the oncologist comes in. She's tall and thin with straight blond hair and is very friendly. She wears high heels and a skirt and blouse underneath her medical coat. She tells me, "Karen, you need to have chemotherapy right away. I want to start you next week."

I'm floored. "Why? I thought I didn't need it."

She explains I have three important factors that she is basing her decision on. Firstly, I am young. I am only 39, and I have cancer. Secondly, my tumor was stage 2. It was over 2 cm in size. And, thirdly, I had lymph node involvement: one of my lymph nodes was infected with cancer. She waits.

I wait.

We talk about the details and determine I will start next week.

I call my mom crying, "I'm going to lose my hair!"

Expansion

Shortly after the second part of my single mastectomy, I have a series of quick, efficient visits with my plastic surgeon as she fills my expander. She knows her stuff.

She finds the expander port. Marks it with a sharpie. Little pinch with the needle and then my breast fills upwards like a balloon.

"I feel these little spurts of pain," I comment.

"That is the skin expanding," she replies. "So, what are we doing with the other breast?"

"Nothing," I say.

She wants me to know my breasts can't be even if I don't do a little lift to my right breast. She informs me my fears of the left staying perky and the right becoming droopy will come true, but I don't want more surgery or stuff inside me which isn't "me." Why should I make a scar on my second breast when it is perfectly fine and beautiful just as it is? I am happy the way I am; she wants me to look good as I age. But, to me, that means additional surgeries in the future and additional scars. I want the implant on the left side to be as even as it can be without doing anything to the right side, so I ask her if instead she can make the left implant droop. She just kind of laughs as if I'm the first person to ever ask such a ridiculous question.

I chose to get an implant and not do any other type of reconstruction because I wanted the fewest scars possible. Additionally, I am thin so I'm not a candidate for many of the options available.

The First One

Today is Friday and is my first round of chemotherapy. I've reached out to a girlfriend who I don't see frequently to take me. I first go to the vitals room and get my blood work done. Then, upstairs on the infusion floor, first things are first: I must provide payment or insurance.

The infusion suite itself is many rooms adjoining one another, and I am led to a light blue recliner, which has a small tan TV attached. I tell the nurse she has to use my right arm for the IV. Since I had lymph nodes removed from my left armpit, I've been trained to always say this to prevent lymphedema from occurring in my left arm. She inserts the needle and hooks me up to my IV, which will be an Adriamycin Cytoxan (AC) cocktail aimed at disrupting the cell functions of any cancer left in my body. My oncologist informed me my chemo will consist of four doses of AC, each two weeks apart for the first two months, and then three months of T (Taxol), each one week apart for twelve weeks. I have been told this is an extremely toxic combination of drugs. I have also been told that I will lose my hair after the first two weeks.

Nothing very exciting happens as I get my drip. I get a little sleepy and take a nap while my friend watches my TV. When it's done, I am told to return the next day for a Neulasta shot, which will boost my immune system and fight infections.

Tennis Anyone?

In my oncologist's office I see a flyer for a tennis group for breast cancer patients. I decide to call and arrange to go to the next meeting. It's Sunday, two days after my first chemo, and I'm feeling pretty good.

I go and meet everyone, and we play tennis with three coaches for an hour. And it's *free!*

I make three friends right away and play with them. Afterward, all the women pile into a little room and sit on kid-sized chairs and have a discussion. They ask me to introduce myself and tell them about my cancer experience, so I do. They inform me they have monthly speakers on various topics related to breast cancer and anyone who has ever had breast cancer can play and attend the meetings. Their oldest member, who still plays, is a ninety-one-year-old breast cancer survivor! They invite me to come back, and I exchange numbers with the girls I played with.

I plan to go again.

Nausea Like You Wouldn't Believe

After I play tennis, I start to become nauseous. I eat crackers, I try ginger, I try ginger candies, I drink Ginger Ale. I try everything I can think of but nothing helps. I am given Zofarin and Lorazepam, but they hardly lessen the overwhelming feeling that my food won't stay down. My appetite starts to dwindle as I am too nauseous to eat. I never throw up; I just can't get beyond the drop in my stomach. I think: if only I would throw up, maybe I would feel some relief? But I never do.

The nausea continues for two and a half months as my chemo progresses and my weight continues to drop. When the AC portion of my treatment is over, I weigh ninety-four pounds of skin and bones.

Losing My Hair

I scream and then laugh. One of my neighbors must be using their water, causing the temperature of my shower to go cold for a moment. The warmth returns, and I begin to lather my hair. I figure my mom is wondering if this time I actually am starting to lose my hair, but I'm not. I continue my shower. I use my shampoo, and as the soap runs down my neck, I notice how silky smooth it feels. While rinsing out the soap, I can feel a few hairs have come loose in my fingers. I rub my neck and feel more. OK, just rub again and these will all come out and then stop, I tell myself. But they don't. I comb through my hair again, and when I bring my hand back before me, there's a clump of dark brown hair in my fingers. *"Ahhhh!"* I scream for real this time. Even though I knew it was coming, I'm still caught in disbelief.

I put the clump on the white tile wall and stop touching my hair.

I leave the hair where it is and turn the water off. Getting out of the shower, I stub my toe and exclaim, "Ouch!"

"Are you alright?" my mom yells in.

My shoulders round and droop and my head falls forward resting on the door. I don't know if I can speak. Finally the words come, "Yeah, I'm OK . . . I started to lose my hair."

"Oh," she says.

Then, I wonder if I should rub my hair with the towel or will that cause it all to fall out? I decide to let it dry naturally.

When I go back later to brush it, the brush fills up with hair, so I stop brushing despite it looking messy.

The next morning, I try once more with the brush, but the same thing happens. "It's time to get my hair shaved," I tell my mother. "Let's go now. I can't deal with these huge clumps of hair coming off in my hands."

Shaving it Off

We go to Super Cuts where it's twelve dollars to shave my head. We wait for a few moments while the stylist gets ready, and the well of emotions comes. I have to give up my hair. I have no choice. It's falling off. The dreaded time has come.

I sit in the chair expecting to watch, but she has me tilt my head down so I can't see. I don't know if she did it on purpose. It's probably just to shave the hair off more properly, I tell myself. "I have several bumps on my head so can you be extra careful of them please?" I say.

I can feel the razor moving across my head. It feels very smooth. But then I feel a clump of dry hair resting on the side of my head, then it slips and falls to the floor. It happens again. And again. I can see myself now and the hair continues to fall. Surprisingly, I'm holding it together pretty well.

We ask the stylist about wigs and wearing caps underneath and she only really knows about the kind of caps that are thin like stockings. I was thinking about getting a thicker one with a wickaway feature that I had heard about.

When it's done, I don't cry. I am still me. But I do ask if the bumps on my head are really noticeable? After all, a woman's head is still a woman's head. I look at my hair on the floor making a circle around the chair. It was still pretty long, even after having cut off the ponytail for Locks of Love a few weeks before. I pick some up. I notice it actually has several colors in it too. It's pretty, I think. OK, so maybe this is gross, but I decide to keep some of what I picked up off the floor. The stylist had asked me before she began if I wanted to save it and I had said no. Now, I decide I want to keep some.

The Bathtub Floor

It comes out every time I shower now. I had thought buzzing it off would fix the problem, but it didn't. So, I had decided not to wash my hair. I figured it would still come out in my bed and in a hat, but at least it would not end up in my hands and all over the bathtub. But since tomorrow is Easter, I decide to wash it today. And here I am again, on my hands and knees, cleaning hairs up off the bathtub floor.

Receiving Cards

My mom picked up my pile of cards and sat down to look at them. "Read them out loud," I say, and so she begins. Some are older, some handmade, some are from my favorite people and make me smile, others are tear-jerkers—but all are comforting in their own way.

Moms

I highly recommend moms! I wish everyone had a mom as wonderful as mine. I know that's not the reality, but in a good world it would be the norm. My mom has cleaned, cooked, organized, supervised, worried, gotten burned, made the bed, done the laundry, used her frequent flyer miles and money, vacuumed, chauffeured, laughed, cried, fed the fish and cat, played with the cat, made phone calls, arranged flowers, dusted, supported, bathed, and cared for me, even sitting with and waiting for me. Did I mention she cared for me every day before, during, and after this surgery? What will I ever do when she leaves?

If One Port's Not Enough—Have Two

I decide to get a chemo port, which is a small medical piece planted in my chest just under the skin and connected to a vein. I don't want to have to be stuck with a needle every time I go for chemo and this instead will mean I will have a small prick in the port to connect to the IV through which I will receive my chemo.

Port surgery is a normal surgery in the same operating room but with a different surgeon. I have my surgery and return home. I'm still nauseous from the chemo but now the nausea increases and progresses to an even more unbearable level. I run to the bathroom and vomit. I check and I have a low-grade fever. I call my surgeon and she orders more antibiotics than I'm already taking.

I come in for my next scheduled chemo and my oncologist looks at my new port, which to me is pink, and she says, "Oh no! That's red and angry! You have an infection."

She refuses to do chemo.

What? No chemo? I don't want to drag on my chemo and this perpetual nausea! But she won't be persuaded.

I'm sent back to have the first port removed and another port added on the other side. They plan to "leave the port open" so I can get my next chemo earlier.

Additional Injuries—Keloids

I have this bump on my hand which I'm told is called a "keloid." It was caused when I had my second port put in and the anesthesiologist jammed the needle in, fast and hard, into the vein on my hand. After the surgery, the bump appeared. My oncologist, today, said to put warmth on it three times a day to help reduce it.

Chemo's Not Fun

My best friend, Alex, and his wife Wendy are visiting this week. They go with me to chemo. Alex stands in front of me because though I had the port put in, I'm still afraid of needles. The nurse comes over and Alex distracts me. He says, "Look at my fingers," and he holds up two fingers in the peace sign and waves them back and forth. The nurse pokes the needle into my port and it doesn't hurt much more than a pinch.

Alex and I talk while Wendy walks to the diner at the corner, and I conclude, "chemo's not fun," as I sit there and get drugs pumped through my veins.

When I'm done for the day, Alex says he has a surprise for me. He leads me to the far side of the lobby and Wendy, at our side, has a big grin on her face. Technically, this is the front side of the cancer center but I don't usually go all the way down the hallway because I enter by the parking garage at the back of the building. Alex stops and standing in a "ta-da" pose points at a beautiful, black baby grand piano. "Do you want me to play you something?" he eagerly asks. Alex, as a child, was a world-famous pianist and producing sound on this piano would bring him as much joy as it would bring me in hearing it.

He proceeds to play. One of the songs he chooses to play is my favorite Chopin song and to his surprise, and Wendy's delight, I start dancing, frail and feeble as I've become. She takes pictures to capture the moment before we head to the car and return home.

180

I Vant to Suck Yur Blud

I'm on Taxol now and my hair is starting to grow back. I get a dose of Benadryl with each infusion which makes me really tired. I'm trying to gain weight, but my mom insists the Fribble I get from Friendly's, which is their version of a milkshake, after my weekly visits to the cancer center is not the right way to gain.

My weekly blood pricks are healing quickly but my hemoglobin levels have started to drop. My oncologist mentions I may need a blood transfusion. *A blood transfusion. This body has never been meant to ever have a blood transfusion.* The thought of having someone's blood pumped into me is just plain disgusting.

I go home but after taking my daily walk—down the block and back at 1 mph—I feel overwhelmingly weak. It's Friday and there's a holiday weekend coming so I call up my doctor and they're able to fit me in during the last slot before they close. As I drive there all I can think of is the color *red*. And when I sit in the recliner, watching the red blood drip down the tube, looking like thick, red milk in a straw, flowing into my port, I can only think, What more can possibly come next?

A Good Cancer Day

Today I accomplished much. I did my laundry and my friend at the laundromat gave me a huge hug—she could tell I had cancer without my even saying it. I also went to play tennis, which I've been able to start again since switching to Taxol, and it was a lot of fun! We had a large lesson and then played "queen of the court" and then "scramble." Several of my friends were there plus women I've never met. One is amazed I am playing tennis while taking Taxol. She said she was not able to function, having had full body aches the entire time. Another woman mentions "Casting for Recovery" which is a fly fishing group for breast cancer survivors—I never had an interest in fishing, but it strikes me as being so much fun . . . and peaceful.

Feeling good and actually able to focus, I listen to the radio without needing to change the station in the middle of each song.

I put most of the laundry away and speak to Daniela. She's sweet; she tells me I was supposed to be letting her do my laundry for me. "That's what I'm coming up there for, to help you, not for you to entertain me," she says. I'm so excited she'll be here soon.

Then I call Alex. I say, "I guess I'm lucky. Even though I needed the blood transfusion, I bounced back pretty quickly."

Alex says it's not about luck. "You have been graced with a strong immune system," he comments, and I agree.

Today I feel like going to bed. I'm tired. I had a good, but long day, and tomorrow should be a good day too with Daniela coming to visit.

Lymphedema #1

I wake up one Sunday morning and notice my left hand is puffy on top. That's weird. I wonder what I could have done to cause it—maybe I ate too much salt. Did I have an infection or bad reaction to a mosquito bite?

Then it hits me ... it's lymphedema! I had twenty-six lymph nodes removed during my mastectomy and wear a compression sleeve on airplanes to prevent my arm from swelling.

I immediately recall I was lifting heavy boxes the night before in preparation for a yard sale and had pulled myself up to reach a high shelf repeatedly. It hadn't even occurred to me to put on my sleeve. The lymph fluid was building up in my hand because it couldn't properly drain up and out of my arm. I was angry that so many lymph nodes had been removed when only one, the sentinel node, had had cancer in it. My doctor had explained lymph nodes are in clumps so maybe she had to take that many? Or maybe, she wanted to be extra certain I didn't have cancer in any of the others since the sentinel was infected? I decide to watch it and see if anything more develops.

My Poor Little Sweetie

My cat doesn't understand. She doesn't understand why I don't play with her. I was reading in bed and she came up and crouched down. I thought nothing of it; she was just watching me. Then she pounced, ripping my hand open!

The next day when one of my doctors saw my hand, he said, "You need antibiotics."

"I do?" I didn't even know if it was her teeth or her claws which had ripped open my hand. It was probably a defensive move to hold up my hands and protect my face and body from the attack.

I try to understand my baby and conclude she just wanted to play, but I no longer seem to have any interest. Have I fallen out of love with my cat—my only baby? Does chemo dull the senses too?

Reconstruction—The Exchange

My last surgery is my "exchange" surgery at which time my expander will be replaced with an implant. I've been coming to my plastic surgeon's office weekly to fill my expander and stretch my skin to fit my implant. Since I was so thin at the time, my only option was an implant. It was also the only thing I had heard of and it required the fewest surgeries and recovery time. I did hear implants need to be replaced every ten years, so I ask my doctor. She informs me it can stay in unless it moves or changes shape or becomes infected.

My mom is here for this surgery again, and though I don't want to have another surgery, I want to get this over with so I'll truly have no more. *For the rest of my life!*

Lymphedema #2

I call my general surgeon today because the slight swelling in my hand is back. I get the unfriendly nurse, and I brace myself since she has always had a harsh temperament. I tell her about the lymphedema and, just as I anticipated, here it comes. She yells at me over the phone: "Are you wearing your sleeve? Are you keeping it elevated?"

I feel belittled. But the truth of the situation is that it's hard to remember to do all these new things that I've never done before. Yes, I'm not supposed to be lifting heavy weights without wearing the sleeve, but I didn't correlate that with pulling myself up to reach a high shelf multiple times. And since I don't move boxes around on a consistent basis, I wasn't accustomed to thinking about putting the sleeve on. There are so many things you don't know about in advance and so much information for caregivers to tell each patient and for each patient in turn to remember. I make an appointment to come in and pray I can avoid her. No one else in this entire experience has offended me so.

Lymphedema #3

My arm is now in pain. I can barely lift it without causing a shooting shock to radiate downward. The hand is starting to swell again too, so I call my general surgeon to move up the appointment. To my surprise, the office redirects me to my plastic surgeon since I "most recently had my reconstruction surgery." I'm dumbfounded, but at least my prayers were answered, and I don't have to see the unfriendly nurse.

I try to "walk the wall" with my fingers since that's the only exercise I know from post-mastectomy, but I'm forced to do it so gingerly. My aim is for ten reps, but I doubt I can even do that many. Pain relievers hardly help.

Lymphedema #4

My plastic surgeon notices the lymphedema and believes the pain I'm having may be due to that too. She wants me to get it taken care of so she gives me a prescription for a physical therapist who specializes in lymphedema. However, the recommended therapist is not in my network. I ask if it's OK to go to a lymphedema specialist someone in my young breast cancer support group mentioned, and I'm given the green light.

I set up an appointment for seven thirty a.m. It means I'll have to get up extra early, but I need to go and it's the only time that will allow me to get to work on time.

My Lymphedema Specialist

Today, I meet my lymphedema specialist. She measures both of my arms to compare them and my left arm is slightly larger than my right. Most of the lymphedema is in my hand. She uses special massage techniques to massage the lymph out. The plan is to teach me how to wrap my hand and arm myself, but for now I'm to wear my sleeve and glove. I am familiar with wearing a sleeve, which I have been instructed to do when flying and lifting heavy objects, but not the glove. She explains to me the purpose of the glove is to prevent the lymph fluid from pooling in the hand and then the sleeve works by moving it up and out of the arm.

Wrapping #1

Wrapping. I used to be a gift-wrap stylist and decorated beautiful packages for the Container Store, but this is not the same. I start practicing by wrapping one white gauze first around my fingers and then around my hand. The second gauze goes around the wrist and fingers and then up the forearm. Next, I put on a compression wrap that looks like an ace bandage, but is not, which goes around the hand and thumb and then up the arm. Two more "ace bandages" follow the first up the arm. I'm wrapping my left arm with my right hand and must not allow the rolls to fly off and unroll. I look like a one-armed mummy as I try to prevent the wraps from zooming off and unrolling by taping the ends as soon as I finish each roll. It is extremely comical, making me think I'm a cartoon character in the fictitious movie *Downfall of the Mummies: Part 1*. It is quite the cumbersome task, and when it's done, my arm and its bandages look so thick.

My homework is to wear it and sleep in it to see if this makes the swelling go down. The next time I go in, I will get the refresher course to see if I can do it on my own.

I head off to work and *everyone* notices it. "What happened?" they say.

I explain that it's for the lymphedema.

"But you were fine yesterday!" they exclaim.

Fine. Yesterday. Yesterday and yester-year are all quite relative to me now.

Wrapping #2

I'm back in my lymphedema specialist's office to get the results. My measurements are slightly down, but my hand is still puffy. She cuts out an orange, hand-shaped piece of foam to add into the wrap to hopefully resolve the swelling.

I practice wrapping. While I do this, my specialist uses an ancient machine that rerolls the wraps. It's wooden with metal rods that stick out to the side—kind of like a giant spool winder. It's much faster than rerolling the wraps myself.

My homework this time is to remove the wrap and redo it as best as I can. I'm concerned I won't do it well, but I have no choice. It seems I haven't had many choices really in this whole process, which seems odd. It's just been put one foot in front of the other and keep going.

Wrapping #3—Membership Has Its Privileges

The true test to see if I had learned how to wrap occurred when I went for the holidays to my parent's house in Tennessee. I would have to wrap my arm each night before going to bed and then take it off each morning, rerolling each wrap in between, to prepare them for the next night.

In Newark Airport the guard at the security check looks at me and pulls me right out of the line. She decides I'm not going through the scanner and she will use the wand on me. It turns out it's all for the best because I get to skip the line.

Then I get to board at the beginning with those who need extra time boarding since I won't be able to lift my bag up to put it in the overhead compartment.

I guess breast cancer does come with some privileges after all.

Everyday Changes

I schedule myself for a massage and a facial, but I don't know if it will hurt to lie on my stomach and have pressure put on my back.

The masseuse gives me an extra pillow to lie on to support my breast and implant.

Little everyday things have to change. Things I never thought about.

I didn't realize either that I can no longer have a true massage for fear of reactivating the lymphedema. I am not allowed to have my left arm massaged at all, and I shouldn't get my back near that arm massaged either, maybe not even the back at all.

The Hot and the Cold

I'm on Tamoxifen now because my cancer was estrogen positive and progesterone positive (ER+/PR+) which means my cancer binds to and grows in the presence of estrogen and progesterone in my body. Tamoxifen is supposed to help prevent the cancer from coming back but it causes random hot flashes.

For so long I was cold all the time, which I think is partly because during chemo I went down to 94 lbs. But now, the hot flashes come. A brief moment before one happens I can feel it coming, but there's no way to stop it nor is there enough time to excuse myself from whatever room, or space, I'm in.

It's hard to explain other than to imagine feeling nice and toasty next to a fireplace—or feeling the steam from a car vent—and then suddenly the comforting heat goes up and up and up, and in a moment, you're overcome by *way too much* heat. My face flushes red, hiding any hope of discretion, and I struggle for a cooling breath. One moment I'm in the car singing along, and the next I need to turn the damn AC on! The feeling swells through my body, overtaking my thoughts and rational feelings. It lasts for what seems an eternity before it subsides and all is back to normal except for the sweat left on my skin.

I wonder if they will continue for the rest of my life since I'm not near true menopause. I ask my oncologist what I can do and she comically says, "buy a fan" . . .

Side EFX

Today, I found out chemo has put me permanently into menopause so I've been switched to Arimidex as my cancer prevention pill of choice. In simplest terms, Arimidex prevents androgen from becoming estrogen so there is less estrogen available in the body. The negative is it can cause muscle and joint pain and is not good for your bones. A friend of mine read on breastcancer.org that Tamoxifen is actually *good* for your bones if you've been through menopause. However, my friend Alex believes Arimidex is the best choice anyway, and he finds it his business to research everything for me and his wife, who is also a breast cancer sufferer. I have also been told glucosamine chondroitin helps with the joint pain, and keeping active with playing tennis, walking, and going to the gym will help too.

It's upsetting to be permanently in menopause, though, because I can no longer have children. My oncologist had asked me during our very first meeting if I wanted to have kids and freeze my eggs but doing so would've meant postponing chemo. I wasn't married, wasn't certain about kids, and she wanted to start chemo the next week. Now, if I had frozen eggs, I wouldn't be able to carry them without adding hormones to my body, which could reactivate the cancer. I know I can always adopt or marry a widowed or divorced man with kids, so I do still have options.

Chapter 6 Tips

Chemo brain

Chemo brain, or cancer-related cognitive impairment, is a side effect of chemo which may be fatigue related, or due to hormonal therapy, cancer treatments, or even anxiety. Also known as chemo fog, it tends to get better over time but can affect a patient's thinking and memory during or after treatment. The Mayo Clinic suggests ways to cope including thinking exercises such as doing crosswords puzzles, joining a theatre group and memorizing lines and poems, reading books, and learning coping strategies and stress-relief techniques.

ACT—Adriamycin, Cytoxan, Taxol

This was my chemo cocktail, which interferes with cells as they are dividing. But it does come with side effects: hair loss, nausea, neuropathy, mouth sores, infertility, menopause, decreased white blood cell count, and infections. Adriamycin can also cause secondary heart problems and shortness of breath.

Hair loss

ACT and many chemotherapy cocktails cause hair loss. Consider keeping some before cutting or shaving it to make a fringe (bangs) on a baseball cap, which is called a "halo." If your hair is long enough, you can attach a ponytail to the back of the cap. I didn't realize even short hair continues to fall out in the shower and on pillows.

One advantage to having hair loss is I didn't have to shave my legs for several months!

197

Eating

I was nauseous for the first three months of chemo and went down to ninety-four pounds. Some people eat more during chemo, but food doesn't taste the same and can have a metallic flavor. Mouth sores can also develop; you can use mouthwash to help this. I was told to try to eat smaller meals and not drink while eating. Also, avoid foods with strong smells or a lot of grease. Ginger sometimes helps and it comes in many varieties.

Neuropathy

Some patients lose sensation and have numbness in their hands and feet. Toenails and fingernails may seem to double and get ridges. My oncologist requested I not paint them.

Teeth

My dentist felt it was important for me to have any dental work I needed prior to chemo.

I also found using a toothbrush during some parts of chemo made me gag and feel like I was going to throw up when it was barely inside my mouth. A friend of mine, who is a cancer survivor, suggested using my finger instead. This worked. Using mouthwash also helped.

Menopause

Some chemotherapy agents can cause pre-mature menopause. Sometimes it is reversible; sometimes it is not. The advantage is not having a period. The biggest disadvantage is not being able to have children. There are also other effects due to a decreased amount of estrogen in the body such as bone density loss, hot flashes, and vaginal dryness.

Freezing eggs

When first meeting with an oncologist, discuss the possibility of freezing eggs. For me this would've meant delaying the start of chemo until I had a period, at which time my eggs could've been harvested. I chose not to wait knowing I can always adopt, marry a man with children, or spend lots of time with my nieces and nephews. And I actually have hundreds of kids right now through my teaching job.

Bone health

Tamoxifen and Arimidex affect bones and bone mineral density. It is important to eat a diet with enough calcium, which is best absorbed from natural sources, to counteract bone density loss. In order to be absorbed, calcium pills also need to be accompanied by Vitamin D3, and it is best in smaller doses. It is important to follow your doctor's guidelines on how much calcium you need.

Good sources of calcium, as listed by Harvard Health Publishing and Harvard Medical School, are:

- Milk, yogurt, and cheese. 1 cup (8 oz.) of milk is equal to 300mg.

- Kale, broccoli, and Chinese cabbage are vegetable sources.

- Figs and oranges are other produce options.

- Fish, such as canned sardines and salmon, with soft bones that you can eat are good animal sources.

- Some breakfast cereals and fruit juices are fortified with calcium.

Bone strength also requires weight-bearing exercises, such as lifting weights.

Temperature changes

I was always cold throughout chemo, and then once I started treatment post-chemo, with Tamoxifen and Arimidex, I started experiencing hot flashes, flushing with heat and then returning to being cold. Sometimes the hot flashes make me sweaty, so then I would be even colder afterwards. Some friends of mine say they wake up with their sheets soaking wet. In my experience, hot flashes lesson over time and some medications can reduce hot flashes if they are severe. To cope you can try a variety of solutions, such as carrying a mini-fan, wearing layers, or using cooling bead necklaces or bracelets.

Dryness

Menopause can cause sexual dysfunction as it causes dryness. Dryness in the vaginal area can also cause labial agglutination (discussed later) though this is not common. Doctors can work with you to help alleviate the dryness.

Lymphedema

For me, lymphedema occurred as swelling in my arm and hand. Lymphedema can develop on the side where axillary surgery occurs, and at least the sentinel lymph node is removed. The swelling is due to the lymph system not being able to move fluids upward and out of the arm. Lymph nodes are gathered in clumps and my sentinel lymph node was positive for cancer. My surgeon then took out a total of twenty-six lymph nodes. Having a greater number of lymph nodes removed elevates the likelihood of lymphedema occurring, but it can occur even if only one lymph node has been removed. Lymphedema can also occur at any time, even many years later. In my experience, the severity of the lymphedema has lessened over time.

I had a bad experience buying a glove. My lymphedema is in my arm and my hand so my therapist instructed me to buy a glove and sleeve. She informed me I should always wear my sleeve with my glove to prevent further swelling in my hand as the glove pushes fluid out of the hand and into the arm and then the sleeve pushes it out of the arm. My representative at the medical supply store ordered a gauntlet for me, not a glove. Unfortunately, when I wore it, I started having greater swelling in my fingers, and I developed an infection between my fingers because the gauntlet pushed my fingers together and they became sweaty. The remedy was the glove as was initially ordered.

My therapist informed me of several additional things. First, I should wear my sleeve and glove whenever I am lifting heavy objects or traveling on airplanes. Second, they should be washed with a mild detergent that does not contain fabric softener, and is not Woolite, and they should be replaced every six months. Third, it's important to avoid infection and trauma to the affected arm and hand; I shouldn't have blood drawn, get injections or an IV, or have my blood pressure taken on that arm. Fourth, I shouldn't get a massage to the affected area and surrounding back unless performed by a therapist who is specially trained in lymphatic massage. And, lastly, gaining weight can make lymphedema worse. She is a wealth of information, and I credit her with the lessening of my lymphedema.

The Mayo Clinic and MD Anderson list precautions you can take to help prevent lymphedema which include, but are not limited to:

- Not lifting more than 5 lbs. with the affected arm

- Avoiding trauma and injury to the affected area, including getting new tattoos

- Not having blood drawn from that arm or blood pressure taken

- Avoiding the sun and protecting from sunburn by using SPF 30 or higher sunscreen

- Keeping the skin dry and moisturized with hypoallergenic, alcohol-free lotions and deodorants

- Using insect repellant to avoid insect bites

- Using an electric razor or cream hair-remover to avoid nicks and cuts while removing hair

- Refusing to cut cuticles and avoid the hand or arm massage during manicures (massage should only be performed by those trained in lymphatic massage)

- Refraining from anything tight on that arm or hand including clothing, such as bras, camisoles, and tops, and jewelry except for wearing a compression sleeve on airplanes and when lifting anything over 5 lbs.

- Using the lightest bra prosthesis possible if you need one

- Avoiding extreme heat or cold to the limb (if you opt to go in a hot tub, keep the limb out of the water and limit exposure to fifteen minutes or less)

- Wearing gloves while doing housework, caring for animals, and gardening and using a thimble for sewing

- Avoiding repetitive motion of the limb and frequently elevating it above the heart

- Getting exercise and keeping body weight down

Consult your physician regarding other health conditions and how they could affect lymphedema.

Reconstruction

After I finished chemotherapy, I wanted to get my expander out and my implant put in immediately so I would be "finished." One thing I didn't know I should consider was the fact I had lost so much weight during chemo. This impacted the size of the implant I received because my plastic surgeon's goal was to match the size of my breasts *as they currently were* and my "natural" breast was smaller than at my normal weight. Months later, once I normalized in weight, my implant is now smaller than my "natural" breast. When my weight fluctuates, my "natural" breast changes while my implant does not; sometimes the change is relatively minimal, so I don't notice the difference. Though I have an implant, I still sometimes find myself stuffing my bra on the implant side, especially when I wear a bathing suit.

Sun exposure

The National Comprehensive Cancer Network states chemotherapy patients can be extra sensitive to the sun. Everyone, including family, friends, and caregivers, should were sunscreen of SPF 30 as skin cancer is the most common of all cancers.

Questions to ask the oncologist

-What kind of chemotherapy will be used and how often? Where will it be administered? What are the benefits of chemotherapy? What are the risks and side effects? How will the side effects be monitored?

-Will I need to go on disability, or can I continue working? What do other people do?

-Is there time to discuss fertility and consider egg harvesting options? What are the risks of taking estrogen in order to harvest eggs? What is the cost to harvest eggs and store them? Does insurance cover this? What are the success rates of harvesting and using the eggs? What happens if the eggs are never used?

-What can be done to protect ovaries and ovarian function during treatment?

-Is it likely I will need a blood transfusion during chemotherapy? Should I bank my blood for possible blood transfusions?

-My cancer is ER+ so can we discuss Tamoxifen and Arimidex? Which do you recommend? How long will I be on it? How does it work? What are the side effects?

Questions to ask the plastic surgeon

-How long will I be in the hospital?

-Can you explain to me what the recovery process is and how long recovery takes? Etc. Will driving be restricted? Etc. (See chapter 3 tips)

-Medications (See chapter 3 tips)

-How many drains am I likely to have? Etc. (See chapter 3 tips)

-Will I have any feeling in my breast(s), nipple(s)?

-What is the risk of infection or rejection?

-Am I restricted in what type of bra I wear?

-I live on the second floor—are stairs a problem?

-How can I tell if I have an infection or my implant has ruptured and leaked? And what do I do if I suspect it has?

Questions to as the radiologist

-Can you explain to me the radiation process? What are the immediate and long-term side effects of radiation?

-Will I need to go on disability, or can I continue working? What do other people do?

-Which specific area will be targeted?

-How does radiation effect my recurrence rate?

-How do I protect my lungs and heart?

-What tests will I have to check for side effects during and after radiation?

-What other doctors do I need in order to monitor my lungs, heart, skin, etc. during and after treatment?

Things families, friends, and caregivers should know

-Know "chemo brain" is true. Patients will forget things for no apparent reason which can be anything from groceries to forgetting someone's name. If you are meeting someone for the first time, take the liberty to introduce yourself in case that person's name is temporarily lost.

-Know during chemo patients may be cold and after chemo may have hot flashes.

-Often cancer patients have sensitive noses so please avoid perfumes and colognes when visiting with friends or family going through treatment.

Things families, friends, and caregivers can do

-Pick up fresh groceries or make food to stock the patient's freezer. Make a food schedule for the patient of when family, friends, and neighbors will deliver food because there will be a lot of times when focus or energy will be lacking.

-Household tasks and cleaning: clean the dishes or the apartment during chemo appointments, mow the lawn.

-Offer child care services. Have a play date with the patient's kids—take them to the park, the movies, or the zoo.

-Go for a walk together. Be aware the patient may walk slowly, but exercise is good at any time.

PART TWO

Two Years Later

Chapter 7—Well, Not Exactly

I t's Back. Well, *not exactly*

I don't mean to scare you, but . . .

It has been two hundred and ninety-four days. Well, really it hasn't but it sounds good—or better to me.

Reality? It's actually been more like one thousand, nine hundred, and forty-nine days, but who's counting? To me it was gone. I thought it was gone. I was told I was cancer free so I knew it was gone. But now it's back. Well, not exactly.

Ca 27–29

After having had cancer, the routine was to have a steady progression of follow-ups with my doctors. My schedule was one time per year with my plastic surgeon, two times per year with my general breast surgeon, and every three months with my oncologist. I had been doing this and recently "graduated" after two years to seeing my oncologist every four months.

At every oncological appointment, they did blood work. My oncologist would review the results and examine me, which included assessing my outward appearance, energy, etc. Routinely, I do my blood work at an outside lab because that is what is covered by my health insurance. I usually call my onc's office a few days in advance to make sure they have received the results.

For this appointment, I realize I forgot to call. So, at 4:55 p.m. the day before the appointment, I try calling and asking if they have received my blood results. No one in the office could be reached but I was told by the center it "seemed" they had the results in the system. However, when I arrive the next morning, my doctor does not have the blood work but gives me a clean bill of health anyway after her assessment. I was concerned, and in sensing my concern, she reminds me of my cancer-free status.

The following week I call to check on my results and the nurse tells me my CA 27–29 markers are slightly elevated. In November, of last year, my levels were at 35. By May, they had dropped to 28, and now, were at 39.5, which is over the cutoff number of 38.3. My nurse tells me it is an often unreliable test and my oncologist wasn't concerned so we should, "repeat it at my next appointment in three months to see if the trend was continuing to go up." I mention that my next appointment was in four months and she seemed unconcerned.

I consulted with my mom and spoke to a friend, and the next day I call back requesting, "Can I repeat my blood work in a month to see if the levels are the same? Will the results change in a month; I know I'm not a doctor?" My nurse speaks to my oncologist and tells me she determined I need to get a CAT scan. It seems when she mentioned my name, my doctor said, "Oh, I know Karen Iverson well!"

This was the new beginning.

CAT Scan Results

My oncological nurse calls me. She says, "Everything is very good, but there is one area where something is going on." My mind raced to the thought: *I have breast cancer again.* "It's not related to your breast cancer," she continued, "but we want you to have an MRI."

Ok, so it's not related to my breast cancer, but it's lighting up and is an area of concern. Do I have a metastasis? I could barely even think. I thought I had reached clear sailing—was I wrong?

A New Cluster of Cells

From the MRI, I learned I have a mass near my rectum. A mass the size of a plum that needs to come out. Is it cancer? Don't know. It's undifferentiated, but the doctor's analysis concludes in him saying, "It needs to come out."

I arrange an appointment, and when I meet with him, he says I have options. I wait for him to say I can wait six months and have another MRI to see if anything has changed, but he doesn't. The options all result in the same bottom line which he repeats to me again, "It has to come out."

The reality is, if he had said I could wait I probably would've found another doctor. But he didn't and he seemed knowledgeable and experienced. He tells me he can do it non-invasively by robot and asks when I want to do it.

This doctor was at a different hospital than where I had all of my breast cancer services, so if it was cancer, I guessed I would change hospitals. I had tried the doctor who was recommended at my prior hospital, but his office wouldn't tell me over the phone if it was even possible to do it noninvasively and they couldn't seem to get an appointment in a reasonable time period, so I had moved on.

For insurance reasons, I chose to have the surgery before the end of the year and this surgeon was able to oblige.

Writing a Will

I want to write a will. I can't believe I didn't write one before my mastectomy, but then I was invincible; I knew I wouldn't die. Everyone told me that anyway, and I guess I am living proof they were right.

This time it's different. It may be irrational, but it all stems from my family tree. My grandfather died when my dad was about thirteen, my dad died when my brother was about thirteen, so *logically*, my brother could die at any time now. It makes pure sense. I always thought it would be my brother for this reason, not wishing anything on him, but irrationally I thought the same would happen to him to continue the pattern, but instead, I got breast cancer and faced mortality. But I made it through. Now, I am sick again, so now, it's simple: simple logic says it will happen to me. Where is Leonard Nimoy when you need him?

So, now that I know I may die, I realize I don't have a will. My surgery is only one and a half weeks away. I am scheduled to write my living will in a few days, but my will hasn't been done. Who will take care of my cat? Who will get my jewelry? This really isn't about the money.

A-gglu-tin . . . *What?*

This may not be the most pleasant subject, but it happens. I started having burning upon urination and a crabby feeling down there. It is Saturday. I think I may have a yeast infection—something I never had before cancer. I know I don't have an STD. By Monday, I am in serious pain. The burning is getting much worse. In the afternoon, I call my primary care doctor, saying I think I have a yeast infection. I am told I can't get an appointment until the next day. I call my gynecologist and am told to come in that evening at 6:15 p.m. I grab my stuff and leave work immediately, barely saying goodbye.

When I arrive, the nurse practitioner asks for a urine sample. I go into the bathroom, hold my breath, and pee into a cup.

In the exam room, the nurse practitioner swabs me. And, oh my god, it feels like someone ripped off part of my vagina.

My gynecologist then comes in and immediately upon examination knows what it is: labial agglutination. My labia are stuck together, covering my urethra, and causing pain upon urination. She explains this happens more frequently in girls but can occur in estrogen deficient adult women— check—who are in menopause—check. She tenderly attempts to pull my labia apart as much as she can and sends me home to continue to treat the affected area. I will return for her to evaluate my progress.

217

A Morbid Realization

At some point, I stop playing with my cat. I don't brush her; I do just the bare minimum—food and sometimes litter. Man, am I bad with her litter; it's amazing she doesn't revolt. But the worst is when I decide I don't love her anymore. I am lying in my bed, and I just feel nothing. I don't want her near me, and yet normally I snuggle with her, cuddling her under my arm every night. The thing is, besides my mom, she's family. She is my only baby, the only kid I may ever have, and now I don't want her near me. I imagine it's the same for other people facing these challenges—the need to separate. The need to disassociate. The need to just be nothing to anyone, be it cat or human. Who cares if I live or if I die? At this moment, I don't.

Nerves Anyone?

Everyone thinks I'll wake up, so I probably will. Will. Last Will and Testament. Crazy. I am nervous for them to open me up and rip out a plum-sized mass of cells that is very happy living and growing on its current tree inside my body. I am telling myself I'm not nervous, but I don't want to have another surgery. I recall saying the same thing the last time I had a big surgery: my expander exchange. "I don't want to do this," I said.

"But you have to," my mother replied. And you will. I will. Last will and . . .

My brain is stuck on that. What would it be like to die? Would I meet God? Would I be reunited with my dad, my uncle, my nanny, my nanie, my pop? Maybe, I would be surrounded by warm, white, golden light as I ascend towards the heavens while angels sing. Maybe, there would be nothing. Darkness. A ceasing of everything. A void. What once was, would be no longer, and my brain would be dead. My body would be ashes and worms would crawl through them. Maybe my spirit will rise out of my body, I will look down from above at myself and say, "Thank you for serving me, I love you, but I don't need you anymore," and then float away into another reality, a better reality, one with peace, a happy environment, my family, and love, and I will understand why we have to go through so much crap on this wonderful planet Earth. Hopefully.

Am I nervous? Am I ready? Those seem to be the questions. I wrote a will just in case I don't wake up, and in case I become a vegetable, I wrote a living will. They're pretty simple documents with the will giving away my assets and the living will saying to pull the plug if I'm considered "brain dead," whatever that really means. I don't want to be a burden on anyone, and I don't want to continue to live if I am not really living. My one grandmother had a stroke and lived the rest of her days in a wheelchair, not speaking and eating her food with a spoon tied to her nondominant hand. Did she know we were there when we visited? Someday I will die, but not now. Right now, I have too much to live for so, plum, get out, and leave me be.

New Age Methodologies—What Lorna Says

Lorna says to send love to myself. Just love myself wholeheartedly. Send love to the cluster of cells: I love you, but I no longer need you. You have served me, but it's time to let you go.

Tomorrow night I'm going to a sound healing. It's the perfect time. I'm going by myself unless anyone else comes along to absorb the healing sounds made by the gongs, singing bowls, and drums. It will be a time to introduce and then release the directions with tobacco. A time to be one with and honor Mother Earth. To forgive and be forgiven. Plus, it's right before Christmas and the start of a new year. Now is the time to rejoice, release, and be cleansed. I can smell the sage and frankincense already. I need this.

The Letter

The pre-operative instruction letter came today. It says:

- Do not eat or drink anything as of midnight—*Yes, I'm now an experienced surgery-er!*

- If you develop a cold, sore throat, cough, fever . . . *well, then you're in BIG trouble*

- You must have a responsible adult drive you home—*That doesn't apply as I'll be staying overnight, but nonetheless, my mom will be there anyway*

- Wear comfortable, loose fitting clothing—*Great, I'll look like I just came from the gym; well, I am going to be beaten up*

- You will be asked to remove personal items:

  o . . . dentures—*really?*

  o . . . contact lenses—*got it, mental note to bring glasses*

- You may use a scrunchie to tie up long hair—*A scrunchie? My computer can't even spell check scrunchie anymore!*

- Don't wear any jewelry, body piercings—*This was hard. I wear my ring every day. It's a connection to my grandmother, and I didn't want to remove it. What about a cross? It's like saying, OK, here I am clean and ready for the morgue. They might as well say, "Please remove all tattoos!"*

- If you are staying overnight and want to bring some personal toiletries, a robe and slippers, please have your family or visitor hold these items until you are admitted into your room—*Don't you wear hospital gowns and socks? And do I really want my slippers to be in a hospital room and bathroom that is probably teaming with bacteria? I will bring my blanket from my classmates, though!*

Included with this letter were the instructions regarding when to arrive. It said I would be called by six p.m. the night before instructing me when to arrive.

9:15 (and a half)

Enough already. I don't know what time the surgery is, and it just makes me more anxious that everybody, and I mean everybody, keeps asking. Everybody, including me, wants something concrete to grab on to. Personally, I want to hold on to it and squeeze it so tight, practically to death, but the hospital for whatever reason can't make up its mind. Or so it seems, as if the hospital is a sentient being.

Well, this is not exactly true. They did give me an approximate time. They just won't tell me the *exact* time until the night before. I wonder if this hospital does this to everybody. I mean, how can you not know what time the surgery is until the night before? Don't people need to make plans? Don't the surgeons need to know? A surgeon must be meticulous, prepared, and planned, but then again I guess they have to be ready to fly by the seat of their pants as well since each body they are working on has its own obstacles. But really, not letting me know what time the surgery is and when I need to arrive until fifteen hours before? What are they afraid of? Don't they realize *I* need to know? I *need* to know. Come on.

My other hospital didn't do this. Though, they did get the time wrong.

Good Old Tennessee

I've spent Christmas at my parents' house in Tennessee, and now we're heading to the airport. My mom is coming home with me for the surgery, which is tomorrow, and my stepdad is heading to South Carolina to be with his ailing mother. I find myself tearing up while I say goodbye to the house. This time it's not goodbye, I'll see ya later—but goodbye, I may never return.

I don't mean to be morbid; it's very likely I'll survive, but I can't help feeling what I feel and the feelings just come. I was once told that an emotion only lasts sixty seconds. If I can get through these sixty seconds, it will pass, unless I ruminate over the situation and then prolong the emotion. I guess when I'm really sad one emotion leads to another.

I drew an image of an emotion once which I still have. At the top is a tiny, *tiny*, elongated triangle representing the thought. Encircled below is the emotion gone wild as illustrated by a cacophony of images crossing and wrapping around one another. Around it, it says, "Don't let a thought become an emotion."

Outside, the rising sun is brilliant. Its golden rays reach towards me with warmth and love. Will this be my last sunrise? Well, actually, I realize I'll have one tomorrow, but I forget for a moment. Will *tomorrow* be my last? Goodbye, Tennessee, may I live to see you again.

The Day After—Surgery #6

OK, surgery sucks; it's official. I thought I would breeze right through this—of course this was during the moments when I didn't think I was going to die—but I guess not. It's hard to breathe because the pain is in my abdomen and I can't take Percocet because it makes me nauseous for hours until I finally throw up. Instead, I'm taking extra strength Tylenol and Zofarin for the nausea, which was unbearable the day I returned home from surgery. This of course brings me right back to my chemo days and dropping to 94 lbs., not something I'd like to repeat. Right now I'm only able to eat in small portions, such as one scrambled egg for breakfast and half a naval orange several hours later. I am able to sit up in bed by my own effort but walking through the living room and into the kitchen is still a hike.

Last night my drain leaked while I was sleeping on my recliner so now I'm afraid my recliner is infested with germs. My mom did her best to clean it and is now sitting on it, so I guess it's OK. I'm sure I'll be sitting on it later anyway, and if not, I know my cat likes to lie on it. In the interim, I'm resting on my bed with a garbage bag under a towel in case the drain leaks again. This sounds rather strange but has actually become a good trick because I can easily slide off the bed when I need to get up with the towel frictionless on the plastic garbage bag.

Day Three Post Op

I'm sitting in a bathtub of two inches of water. My mom put my Elemis Super Aching Muscle Soak in the water, and it smells heavenly. I would like to dunk all the way down, but I am still not allowed to get the incisions wet. My hair feels nasty, all heavy and plastered to my head after three days of not being washed. At least I'm in the tub and enjoying the aroma.

Today, I will see my doctor for the first time since the surgery. He's supposed to remove my drain. The liquid now looks hot pink, less bright red, which is good, but there was a lot of fluid in it this morning. Most people seem to hate their drains but mine isn't a love-hate relationship. Because I don't have to do anything social right now, I can just hide it in the pockets of my sweats while I hang around the house so it doesn't bother me as much. Yet, still, I'm afraid he may leave it in for a while longer and the simple fact is: I would like to take a shower.

Appearances

My "wounds" look horrible. When I glance down, I see dark purple rectangles stretching across my flat, pale stomach. What once was beautiful has become a Halloweenish punching bag. I turn my head away, wishing I hadn't seen it.

Longing for My Bed

I'm trying to sleep in my bed but lying on my right side is painful. Lying on my left feels like my ribs are puncturing my lungs. Lying on my back feels like I'm in a torture chamber being stretched, pulling on the wounds on my stomach. I'm forced to resort to my recliner. On the recliner, I can rest on my back with my body more curved at an angle, giving me less pull on my stomach. I stare longingly at my bed. How comforting would it be to be snuggled up in my bed under the warm winter blankets?

My cat doesn't care; she wants to snuggle with me anywhere. I have the forethought to rest a pillow across my lap just before she jumps up on the arm of the recliner. She licks my face as if saying, "Mommy, it's ok." But I still long for my bed. Soon, I think. Soon.

My Office Sent Flowers

My current job, which I've been at for a year and a half now, sent me flowers and a card that everyone signed. They don't really know what's going on. I never told them about the cancer other than mentioning that I had an illness in the past and potentially cluing them in by the fact that I started with pretty short hair, which I've been growing ever since. I told them I had donated it, which I did, and was growing it to donate again, which I am. I merely failed to mention that I did it shortly before it fell out due to chemo.

It's a very small start-up with seven to eight of us in the office each day and I told my boss I would be in the hospital for one to two days for a robotic surgery. Worst-case scenario if they have to switch to invasive surgery I would be in the hospital for three to four days. But, as things turn out, my doctor now is not ready to send me back. He said I can start driving on local roads but not on main highways. I asked him, "What about work then?"

He replied, "We'll talk about that when I see you next week."

So, now I'm trying to reach my boss to let her know. I could maybe arrange to get my laptop home and do some work, but if my doctor doesn't think I'm ready, then should I really be trying so hard? Maybe, I should just sit here in a basically stress-free environment and let my insides heal instead of stressing them into knots in the environment of my job. The reality is I need to accept this was a major surgery; I keep skipping over that fact, trying to be superwoman like I usually do.

Karen, slow down.

Take a deep breath—though not too deep 'cuz it'll hurt.

Take this moment as a bonus:

> Time to reflect.
>
> Time to have peace.
>
> Time to heal.

Flittering Ribbons of Transparent Light

I sit here this morning watching the smoke rise from my incense stick. It stands vertically out of a lotus flower with a little praying, meditating Buddha beside it. The smoke wafts upward and then dances, swirling in the various air currents possibly caused by the drafty window and that of my breath. The smoke varies in color like a subtle rainbow of transparent whites, grays, yellows, and blues. I've never noticed how beautiful it is before. I feel calm and think I need to incorporate more stillness, maybe meditation, into my life again like I used to do years before. The smoke moves like fairies dancing: changing, swirling, each moment unique. I used to feel like that, like beauty surrounded me, like beauty was within me. It's not that I don't feel that way now, it's just that I'm so far away from when I once was so innocent and open.

My body has backed up. My bowels are blocked. I've tried everything from Metamucil, to Senakot, to enemas. Last night I went to Whole Foods and ate a kale, almond milk, and berry smoothie. I also ate kale salad, and creamed kale, and almonds, and olives. I ate broccoli. I threw in some sweet potato after the advice of a friend and a few roasted Brussels sprouts and sesame sugar snap peas just because they looked so good. I was rewarded in the pleasure of their flavors, but alas no BM. I haven't been feeling bad before now, but all of a sudden I'm starting to feel worse. I called my doctor this morning to ask him for some help and the nurse is going to call me back. So, here I sit enjoying the aroma, mesmerized by how the smoke splits from this thin ribbon of transparent light and then twirls like a scroll through the air. This powerful air which we so often fail to acknowledge for providing the sustenance of our lives.

Asking for Help

I decide to go to my young breast cancer support group. It's a great group—geared at young breast cancer survivors, generally under the age of forty-five. Everyone speaks back and forth for at least an hour about losing their hair, shaving their heads, and getting wigs. Finally, I say to the facilitators, "Can we redirect?" I needed help. I wanted to talk about what was going on with me, but I didn't know how to start. So, I tell them I have a tailgut cyst and say, "Maybe you can ask me questions?" It works. They ask me how I am feeling. How did I find it? How long will my recovery be? And the biggie: is it related to my breast cancer? Maybe someone else would shy away from these direct questions, but for me, it is exactly what I need. I need to be heard. They also bring up suggestions and thoughts that I hadn't thought of.

With my breast cancer, I only told some people, but with this, it seems I'm telling everyone. This time the added support is welcome.

Magnesium Citrate

The nurse spoke to my doctor who said to try magnesium citrate to resolve being backed up. At first it didn't seem to do anything, but then it did and now it continues to do so. Magnesium Citrate, I looked up, is a bowel cleanser and my bowels were proceeding to empty. I'm staying near the bathroom and wearing a pad, as if I have my period, for just-in-case moments. I'm starting to fear my bowels will never return to normal but recall my nurse saying to give it two days. I have one more day to go. So, I'm playing the waiting game and wishing for normalcy.

Today's Adventure

Today, I try going for my first real walk since my latest surgery. I walk and listen to tunes and start to sing along—nothing strenuous—but my lungs and ribs start hurting. Maybe it's too cold out? Probably, it's a result of the surgery and breathing shallow breaths for a week and a half, I think. Baby steps.

The Dalai Lama

The Dalai Lama said the purpose of life is to always search for happiness. I like this idea but I know that during this battle, at times, I have consciously chosen the dark side. I have chosen to wallow in my misery for a time. My friends say how I'm so "strong" and am handling this so well, but they don't always see me at the bottom because I don't always show it. Everybody has their moments, I rationalize.

Searching for happiness has to do with eliminating paths towards suffering and enhancing paths towards joy. For example, I start getting nauseous—I try doing meditative breaths. It helps. Maybe that's the first step towards enlightenment.

The Courage to Teach and Heroes

My friend calls me her *hero*. She says in a text message: "I really admire your strength. I don't know how you remain so calm and poised through all this."

Um, because I have to? I mean, isn't this how everybody feels? Calm and collected on the outside and screaming on the inside?

When I was a master's student at Columbia University Teachers College I wrote part of my final paper about *The Courage to Teach* by Parker J. Palmer. He spoke about how teachers are up in front of students—who consider them experts—scared to death the students will figure out they're frauds and don't know the material or how to teach it.

I don't know who or how else to be. I'm going through this. Some days are painful, physically and emotionally, and I'm irrational. Others are painless but I'm overcome with depression. My face tends to frown more than it used to and there are worry lines which no longer easily go away. The unevenness of my lips isn't a concern anymore. Pain and perfection have lost some of their meaning.

I stand up to this now because there is no other way.

But my friend *works overnight, and on the weekends, and is a full-time student* and yet I'm *her* hero. I get through this because I have to. I get through this because I will.

Happiness is having a positive attitude. It is taking a difficult time and eliminating the suffering. Through this entire journey I have suffered, but in looking back, I don't think badly about the experience. I forgive and forget the suffering and focus on the fact I am still alive. I fought to still be here so I can continue to share with others.

My best friend has a dog named Oly. Oly found Alex when he pushed Alex out of the way of an oncoming bus. Alex tried to find his owner but was unsuccessful and Oly didn't have a chip, so he became Alex's dog. Oly was his hero.

Men and women go off to war and fight for our country. Some come back victorious; some sacrifice their lives. They are heroes.

Is someone who fought for their own life and won truly a hero? Maybe. Maybe it all has to do with our own personal point of view. Maybe I am a hero. Maybe, we all are.

D Day

I'm anticipating tomorrow when I see my doctor in his office for the second time since returning home from the hospital. It's D day I suppose; I'll find out the pathology results. No one will be with me when I meet my doctor, but in a way, my mom will be as I'll patch her in through speaker phone. This is the first step towards facing my next journey. I'll have the support I need no matter what the outcome, but I guess I want a private moment to digest whatever may come forth be it good or bad without an entourage of questioning stares. I'll take this moment to stand firm on my own two feet, to feel whatever emotions bubble to the surface, and face them when I'm ready to move on. My doctor and everyone else are anticipating this is not malignant and we shall see if the book is closed or another chapter is added to my story . . .

Finally, the End

To finish the story, I went to the doctor and didn't go alone and found my cyst was a benign tailgut cyst which needed no further treatment.

I looked up "tailgut cysts" and found Haydar and Griepentrog explained they are a rare congenital malformation which may present in the presacral space and are usually asymptomatic, unless infected. They can present at any age but often do between thirty and sixty years old and excision is advised to rule out malignancy, prevent transformation into a malignant state, and prevent getting infected, and also they can cause problems when defecating. Therefore, there is considerable risk for serious illness if left untreated. As my doctor said, it needed to come out.

Chapter 7 Tips

Some thoughts on why we suffer:

I find the following verses from the NIV Bible give insight into why we suffer:

Suffering leads to perseverance:
Not only so, but we also glory in our sufferings, because we know that suffering produces perseverance (Romans 5:3).

Perseverance leads to a mature and complete individual:
Let perseverance finish its work so that you may be mature and complete, not lacking anything (James 1:4).

Our current troubles lead to an eternal glory:
For our light & momentary troubles are achieving for us an eternal glory that far outweighs them all (2 Corinthians 4:17).

Grief leads us to show our faith which leads to the salvation of our souls:
In all this you greatly rejoice, though now for a little while you may have had to suffer grief in all kinds of trials. These have come so that the proven genuineness of your faith–of greater worth than gold, which perishes even though refined by fire–may result in praise, glory and honor when Jesus Christ is revealed. Though you have not seen him, you love him; and even though you do not see him now, you believe in him and are filled with an inexpressible and glorious joy, for you are receiving the goal of your faith, the salvation of your souls (1 Peter 1:6–9).

Questions to ask the oncologist

-Should my blood be tested for tumor markers? How often should I be tested? What are tumor markers and what does it mean if they are elevated? Are tumor marker readings accurate?

30 Day Positive Mindset Challenge

This book is aimed to help breast cancer patients and their loved ones lessen their suffering during this tumultuous period of time. In the tips sections I have listed methods to reduce stress but just reading those methods won't result in finding peace. It's now your turn to take the bull by the horns, if you will, and make a transformation happen by accepting my challenge to form new habits. I have found the hardest thing is to start doing something but then, once I've begun, I'm fine and actually enjoy whatever it is I'm doing (even cleaning). I call this my hurdle effect. I just need to get over the first hurdle and I'm on my way.

Below are 4 simple actions, each take less than five minutes, and if repeated every day for 30 days result in sustainable habits. So right now put this in your planner for tomorrow. And if you're finding yourself hesitating or have a concern you won't be able to continue for 30 days that's normal. Hal Elrod in *the Miracle Morning* explains this nervousness is only signifying you are ready to proceed because otherwise you wouldn't be nervous.

Here's how you begin:

1. Meditative Breathing—When you first wake up in the morning focus on your breathing. Pay attention to your breathing and complete 10 rounds of circle breathing.

    1. Inhale slowly through your nose while you count to four.
    2. Hold for four.
    3. Exhale through your mouth for four.
    4. Hold for four.

With each inhale, imagine white healing light coming in; during each exhale, imagine black smoke exiting, taking all the toxins out.

2. Mirror Affirmations–Walk into the bathroom and before taking your shower, stand before the mirror. Look at yourself and speak to yourself with love. Tell yourself 3-5 affirmations and repeat them 10 times. Look yourself in the eyes when you do this, speak out loud, and say them slowly. Really mean it when you say them.

Here are some examples of my affirmations:

I am healthy.
I am happy.
I am beautiful.
I can do all things with the help of... (fill in here...my spouse, my friends, my mother, God, my higher power, my spirit).

Feel free to adapt them to your choosing.

3. Tell a Friend–*Do this step by 6pm each day.*

For the Breast Cancer patient – tell someone 1 thing that you are concerned about and 1 thing you are happy about. This can be done in a text, over the phone, or by email and to whomever you choose. You can even message yourself!

For loved ones- Send one encouraging sentiment to the breast cancer patient. One word or one phrase only. You can vary how you send this each day (text, email, snail mail). It is important to know sometimes the person going through cancer will be overwhelmed and will not want to talk or, as strange as it sounds, may feel bombarded by everyone calling them. This is a way to say you care without overwhelming the warrior and the warrior can look at the message whenever she wants and as frequently as she wants.

Example sentiments are:

You can do this! I'm here for you! You're strong! Warrior! Peace! Faith! Love you! You're doing great!

4. Total Mind Dump–Just before turning in for the night take your journal, a piece of paper, your computer, your phone, your iPad, or likewise and write down everything that is on your mind. Everything. Yes, I mean everything. Just like in the Chapter 3 Tips section write whatever comes to mind. This can include what happened today, anything you're afraid of or concerned about, everything you're happy about and grateful for, etc. You can take as much time or as little time as you would like to do this. Start with 5 minutes and then work your way up to more.

The goal of this is to help completely empty your mind so you can find some tranquility and hopefully sleep.

Doing the 30 Day Positive Mindset Challenge will allow you to find some peace and harmony and create a sustaining habit that you can continue when you're well. You can do this! If I can do it, you can too. I have confidence in you!

Write Day 1 in your planner now! And see my Special Invitation.

Some Heroes Who Have Helped Me (Resources)

American Cancer Society—education, support, wigs

(https://www.cancer.org)

Beautiful Self—free photo shoots to empower women with breast cancer

(https://www.beautifulself.org)

CancerCare—provides financial support (https://www.cancercare.org)

Cancer Positive—inspiring stories for cancer sufferers

(http://becancerpositive.org)

Caring Bridge—website to disseminate information to love ones

(https://www.caringbridge.org)

Casting for Recovery—free fly fishing retreats (castingforrecovery.org)

Chemo Angels—support (https://www.chemoangels.com)

Cleaning for a Reason—free cleaning services

(https://cleaningforareason.org)

Compassion Partners—free Universal Studios or Sea World tickets
(407–396–5320)

Fighting Pretty—"pretty" packages with pink boxing gloves ($30 donation)
(https://www.fightingpretty.org)

France Luxe—free scarf (goodwishesscarves.org)

Grants—

Beauty Foundation for Cancer Care
(http://www.beautyfoundationnj.com)

The Samfund (http://www.thesamfund.org)

Hair to Stay—Scalp cooling system (http://www.hairtostay.org)

Live Strong—support, resources, free YMCA weight lifting program
(https://www.livestrong.org)

Locks of Love—takes hair donations and gives free wigs to children
(https://locksoflove.org)

Look Good Feel Better—free makeup and class (lookgoodfeelbetter.org)

Peapod*—grocery delivery for a fee (https://www.peapod.com)
  *Many stores will now deliver as well.

Peninsula Medical—free alert band for lymphedema (reidsleeve.com)

Sharsheret—support for women of Jewish descent
  (https://sharsheret.org)

Stupid Cancer—support for patients under 40 (https://stupidcancer.org)

TFL—Tennis for Life–free tennis (http://www.tennisforlife.org)

TLC**—tender loving care–American Cancer Society– wigs for purchase
  (https://www.tlcdirect.org)
  **Local American Cancer Society offices often have free wigs

Vacations and retreats—free or financially assisted
  Camp Make-A-Dream (https://www.campdream.org)
  Epic Experience Beyond Cancer (https://www.epicexperience.org)
  First Descents (firstdescents.org)
  Harmony Hill Healing Retreat (https://www.harmonyhill.org)
  Mary's Place by the Sea (https://www.marysplacebythesea.org)

Project Koru (https://www.projectkoru.org)

Send It Foundation—ages: 18–40
(https://www.senditfoundation.org)

Waves of Grace (https://www.waves-of-grace.org)

Yoga— Yoga for Cancer (https://y4c.com)

Give Back Yoga (https://givebackyoga.org)

My cancer center and other local hospitals offer free support groups, art therapy, yoga, cooking classes, etc.

Afterword

So, what has changed in my life since the cancer? I have more friends—many breast cancer survivors—and I truly know whom I can count on. I spend my money more freely—buying things I need and going out for a bite to eat. I used to be so careful about what I ate. *Is that fattening?* I would check before choosing it. I eat red meat and chicken now, whereas for twenty years I was a pescatarian. During chemo, I thought I needed more protein and so began eating more chicken, and then one day red meat was placed in front of me, so I ate it and never stopped. I do eat more vegetables now versus my prior penchant for carbs, and I mostly eat a lot of salads. Dessert tempts me despite the fact I'm supposed to avoid sugar. I am still very conscious about gaining weight but now it's sometimes harder to stop myself. With everything I make an effort to do it in moderation, including alcohol. And I *always* wear sunscreen! I do recommend any cancer sufferer consult their doctor and nutritionist for eating guidelines as I am not a doctor and am not proposing others follow my eating habits. Overall, I guess I take more risks, feeling the need to live my life and enjoy it.

I've noticed I rarely refer to my cancer as simply "cancer." Because in saying "breast" first, it takes away the impact of "cancer." I don't *feel* like I had cancer; I feel healthy and I consider myself to be. The only difference is I now have a breast with an implant in it and several scars.

How do I feel about God? Well, I don't blame God for making me ill. I think maybe society is responsible. But for several years, I didn't feel as close to God as I had been either. I allowed others to pray for me and sometimes would ask them to do so. Now, I pray—asking for help myself.

The good news is I am now six years cancer free! I count from when I finished chemotherapy and all the cancer was gone.

A Special Invitation

Receive tools from this book FREE!

READ THIS FIRST

Just to say thank you for buying my book, I would like to give you several resources 100% FREE!

Resources include:

30 Day Positive Mindset Challenge Tracker Form

and

Initial Questions to Ask Your Surgeon Form.

To download these FREE resources go to:

www.winningthebreastcancerbattle.com/free

References

Foreword

National Breast Cancer Foundation Inc. (2016). Retrieved from:

https://www.nationalbreastcancer.org/

Chapter One

American Cancer Society. (2019). Cancer facts & figures 2019. American

Cancer Society (2019). Retrieved from:

https://www.cancer.org/content/dam/cancer-org/research/

cancer-facts-and-statistics/annual-cancer-facts-and-figures/

2019/cancer-facts-and-figures-2019.pdf

Chapter Two

American Cancer Society. (2017) Lifestyle-related breast cancer risk

factors. Retrieved from:

https://www.cancer.org/cancer/breast-cancer/risk-and-

prevention/lifestyle-related-breast-cancer-risk-factors.html

Chapter Three

American Cancer Society. (2017). How common is breast cancer?

Retrieved from:

https://www.cancer.org/cancer/breast-cancer/about/how-

common-is-breast-cancer.html

Cameron, J. (1992). The artist's way: A spiritual path to higher creativity. New York, NY: Jeremy P. Tarcher/Putnam.

Barnes, E. (2008). 101 ways to clean out the clutter. Eugene, OR. Harvest House Publishers.

Barnes, pp. 48.

Lambert, M. (2001). Clearing the clutter: For good feng shui. London, England: Cima Books.

Barnes, pp. 17.

Barnes, pp. 63.

Chapter Five

Camus, A. (1960). Resistance, rebellion, and death. New York, NY: A.A. Knopf.

Breastcancer.org. (2019). Bone strength after menopause. Retrieved from: https://www.breastcancer.org/tips/menopausal/longterm_conc/bone_strength

Chapter Six

Mayo Clinic. (1998–2019). Chemo brain. Retrieved from: https://www.mayoclinic.org/diseases-conditions/chemo-brain/symptoms-causes/syc-20351060

Harvard Health Publishing. (2010–2019). Retrieved from: https://www.health.harvard.edu/staying-healthy/how-much-calcium-do-you-really-need

Mayo Clinic. (1998–2019). Lymphedema. Retrieved from:

    https://www.mayoclinic.org/diseases-conditions/lymphedema/

    symptoms-causes/syc-20374682

MD Anderson. (2019). 8 tips for coping with cancer-related lymphedema.

    Retrieved from:

    https://www.mdanderson.org/publications/cancerwise/6-

    tips-for-coping-with-cancer-related-lymphedema.h00–

    158906967.html

Breastcancer.org. (2019). Reducing lymphedema and flare-up risk:

    Things to avoid. Retrieved from:

    https://www.breastcancer.org/treatment/lymphedema/reduce_

    risk/avoid

National Comprehensive Cancer Network. (2019). Take precautions

    During cancer treatment in warmer weather. Retrieved from:

    https://www.nccn.org/patients/resources/life_with_cancer/

    managing_symptoms/summer_precautions.aspx

Cleveland Clinic. (2015). Sun damage: Protecting yourself. Retrieved

    from:

    https://my.clevelandclinic.org/health/articles/5240-sun-damage-

    protecting-yourself

Chapter Seven

His Holiness the 14th Dalai Lama of Tibet. Compassion as the source of

    happiness. Retrieved from:

    https://www.dalailama.com/messages/compassion-and-

    human-values/compassion-as-the-source-of-happiness

Palmer, P. (2007). The courage to teach: Exploring the inner landscape

    of a teacher's life. San Francisco, CA: Jossey-Bass.

30 Day Challenge

Elrod, H. (2017). The miracle morning: The not-so-obvious secret

    guaranteed to transform your life. Hal Elrod International, Inc.

Afterword

Haydar, M. & Griepentrog, K. (2015). Tailgut cyst: A case report and

    Literature review. *International Journal of Surgery Case Reports,*

    10, 166–168. doi:10.1016/j.ijscr.2015.03.031

Louden, J. (2007). The life organizer: A woman's guide to a mindful year.

    Novato, CA: New World Library.

About the Author

Karen Iverson is proof breast cancer does not have to be a debilitating disease destroying a positive mindset. At age 39, Karen was diagnosed with invasive ductal carcinoma and faced potential mortality with grace and courage. Despite dropping to an extremely low weight during chemotherapy, Karen now considers herself healthy and her doctors agree. Always dreaming of using her writing skills and being an author, she chose to share her experiences to help fellow breast cancer patients, their families, and friends.

Karen was born in New York City where she lived until she was 10 and then her upbringing continued in New Jersey. She was often found in her bedroom writing poems and song lyrics, as well as journaling, in spiral bound notebooks. She recalls learning how to "show not tell" her senior year in high school. Karen further developed her techniques as an undergraduate at the University of New Hampshire where she loved her writing classes. She returned to live in NYC as an adult where she acquired her Master of Arts in education from Columbia University Teachers College.

Karen states that she has always been a writer at heart and is honored to have been recognized as a "Difference Maker" at the 2019 Author Advantage Live conference.

Thank you for reading my book.

If you have enjoyed this book please leave a review on Amazon so that others with this disease can find the help they need.

I really appreciate hearing your feedback and
I love hearing what you have to say.

www.winningthebreastcancerbattle.com
winingthebreastcancerbattle@gmail.com

Made in the
USA
Lexington, KY